MATHS SKILLS

for

SCIENCE

YEARS 5&6
Scottish Primary 6—7

CREDITS

Author
Louise Petheram

Editor
Joel Lane

Assistant Editor
David Sandford

Series Designer
Lynne Joesbury

Designers
Rachel O'Kane, Paul Roberts

Cover photography
© Stockbyte

Illustrations
Paula Martyr

Published by Scholastic Ltd,
Villiers House,
Clarendon Avenue,
Leamington Spa,
Warwickshire CV32 5PR

Printed by Alden Group Ltd, Oxford

© Scholastic Ltd 2003
Text © Louise Petheram 2003

1 2 3 4 5 6 7 8 9 0   3 4 5 6 7 8 9 0 1 2

British Library Cataloguing-in-Publication Data
A catalogue record for this book is available from the British Library.

ISBN 0-439-98310-X

Teachers should consult their own school policies and guidelines concerning practical work and participation of children in scientific experiments. You should only select activities which you feel can be carried out safely and confidently in the classroom.

INTRODUCTION   4

PLANNING GRID: YEAR 5   8

PLANNING GRID: YEAR 6   9

YEAR 5

SOLVING PROBLEMS   10

MEASURES   16

SHAPE AND SPACE   28

RECORDING AND ORGANISING DATA   34

HANDLING AND INTERPRETING DATA   46

YEAR 6

ENQUIRY AND INVESTIGATION   64

SOLVING PROBLEMS   70

MEASURES   76

SHAPE AND SPACE   88

RECORDING AND ORGANISING DATA   94

HANDLING AND INTERPRETING DATA   106

RESOURCE PAGES   124

Acknowledgements

The National Curriculum for England 2000 © Crown Copyright. Reproduced under the terms of HMSO Guidance Note 8. **The National Numeracy Strategy: Framework for Teaching Mathematics** © Crown Copyright. Reproduced under the terms of HMSO Guidance Note 8. **A Scheme of Work for Key Stages 1 and 2: Science** © Qualifications and Curriculum Authority. Reproduced under the terms of HMSO Guidance Note 8. **Scottish 5–14 Guidelines for Environmental Studies** © Crown copyright. Material is reproduced with the permission of the Controller of HMSO and the Queen's Printer for Scotland.

INTRODUCTION

WHY SCIENCE NEEDS MATHS

Maths Skills for Science: Years 5&6/Primary 6–7 aims to assist teachers of children aged 10–11, and is one in a series of three books covering the whole primary age range. This book, and the others in the series, have been designed to develop links between the maths taught in the National Numeracy Strategy and the science topics taught in the QCA Schemes of Work, the National Curriculum for Wales, the National Curriculum for Northern Ireland and the Scottish National Guidelines on Environmental Studies 5–14. The books are thus equally valuable to teachers working in all parts of the UK.

The books recognise that for children to be effective learners, they need to develop numeracy skills and science skills in parallel. The present guidelines do not always make the links between science and maths particularly clear, and teachers often find that children need to use particular maths skills within their science lessons that they have not yet learned in their numeracy work. This forces the teacher to use science time in teaching maths skills, leading to a reduction in the 'science value' of the lessons.

'Almost every scientific investigation or experiment is likely to require one or more of the mathematical skills of classifying, counting, measuring, calculating, estimating, and recording in tables and graphs. In science pupils will, for example, order numbers, including decimals, calculate simple means and percentages, use negative numbers when taking temperatures, decide whether it is more appropriate to use a line graph or bar chart, and plot, interpret and predict from graphs.'
Introduction to the NNS *Framework for Teaching Maths*, p17 (March 1999)

Many teachers overcome this problem by co-ordinating their teaching of maths and science to ensure that the relevant maths skills are taught before they are needed in science, or that science topics are taught to reinforce skills learned in maths lessons. But the planning for this can be complicated and time-consuming. The *Maths Skills for Science* books offer a series of co-ordinated maths and science activities that do the planning for you. In addition, the skill levels of the activities are planned to ensure that:

■ the science topics do not require any maths more advanced than that covered in the National Numeracy Strategy for the appropriate year
■ the relevant maths skills are used and reinforced in the science topics.

Developing the maths skills
Progression is built in throughout the series so that the children progress naturally through the skills they need to learn, consolidating and practising at each stage.

Measuring
The activities in the 'Measures' section encourage the children to think about what they need to measure, what apparatus they need to take the measurements, and whether or not the values they record will be accurate. These skills are developed throughout the three books. The children in Years 5 and 6/ Primary 6–7 practise choosing and using apparatus to measure to a suitable degree of accuracy in a range of different measuring tasks. They are also given practice in making decisions about the values they need to measure, and the number of measurements they need to take in order to collect evidence to test a prediction.

Handling data
Although children may collect results successfully from their science activities, they often find it hard to decide on clear and appropriate ways to present their findings. National tests in science have shown that many children's interpretation skills

lag behind their skills in other areas, and it is common for children to experience difficulty in deciding what conclusions they can draw from their work. For this reason, *Maths Skills for Science* concentrates on the whole process of making results meaningful, recognising that this process involves using both maths and science skills.

In these books, the 'Handling Data' strand of the National Numeracy Strategy has been divided into two sections: 'Recording and Organising Data' and 'Handling and Interpreting Data'. These are distinct and specific skills that all scientists need to acquire.

The 'Recording and organising data' section focuses on teaching children to think about why they are presenting their results, to identify the important features they wish to show, and to select the best way of organising their results to make these aspects clear to a reader.

In Years 5 and 6/Primary 6–7), the children present data in tally charts, bar graphs, line graphs, pie charts and probability scales. They make decisions about how to present information as clearly as possible, choosing appropriate scales to use on the axes for bar graphs and line graphs.

In the 'Handling and interpreting data' activities, the children are challenged to ask themselves: 'What do these results really mean? What do they tell us?' In Years 5 and 6/Primary 6–7, the children draw and interpret bar graphs, line graphs (including ones that do not present straight lines) and Carroll diagrams, using these to make comparisons, test predictions and solve problems. They also consider the accuracy of their results, whether there is sufficient evidence to draw conclusions, and ways to improve their investigations or activities.

ABOUT THIS BOOK

The grids on pages 8–9 show how the units in this book are linked both to the maths skills areas of the National Numeracy Strategy and to the science topics in Year 5 or Year 6/Primary 6–7. The main learning objectives for both maths and science are given for each unit in the grid.

The units in the book cover the full range of science topics, with at least one unit for each science topic in each year. Where there are two units for any science topic, these will reinforce or practise different maths skills. An 'Enquiry and investigation' unit has been introduced in Year 5 to cover QCA Unit 5/6H: Enquiry and investigation in environmental and technological contexts. This unit concentrates on two specific activities: one in an environmental context, the other in a technological context. The unit can be completed at any time during Year 5 or Year 6, but could be used as an introduction to either of two Year 6 science topics: 'Interdependence and adaptation' and 'More about dissolving'.

The activities in each book are divided into sections, based on the skill areas highlighted in the National Numeracy Strategy. In this book, the skill areas covered are:
- Solving problems
- Measures
- Shape and space
- Recording and organising data
- Handling and interpreting data.

In this book, it is assumed that the majority of children will have mastered the basic number skills and measurement skills they will need for their science work. The emphasis is on developing an increasing understanding of how measurement can be used to test scientific ideas. The children develop their skills in recording and presenting data in a variety of forms, and in interpreting data to test predictions and draw conclusions.

The activities for each year group assume that the children will achieve approximately Level 3–4, or Scottish Level B/C at the end of Year 5/Primary 6, and Level 4, or Scottish Level C by the end of Year 6/Primary 7. Extension activities are provided for more able children, and support activities for less able children.

Each section contains one or more six-page units. Each unit is focused specifically on a science topic from one of the two years covered, and uses maths skills developed within the National Numeracy Strategy for that year. Each unit is made up of two pages of teacher's notes and four supporting photocopiable pages, as detailed below.

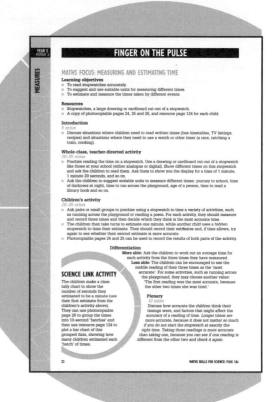

A maths lesson planning page containing:

▣ Learning objectives derived from the National Numeracy Strategy

▣ a suggested introduction and an initial whole-class, teacher-directed activity

▣ a follow-up children's activity consisting of individual or group work

▣ ideas for differentiation for more able and less able children.

▣ a 'Science link' activity that provides maths resources to reinforce the skill taught in the maths lesson within a science context.

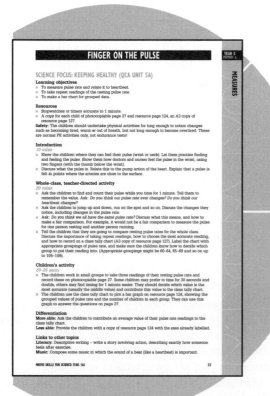

A science lesson planning page containing:

▣ Learning objectives derived from the QCA Schemes of Work or the corresponding documents for Scotland, Northern Ireland or Wales

▣ a suggested introduction and whole-class, teacher-directed activity.

▣ a follow-up children's activity consisting of individual or group work.

▣ ideas for differentiation for more able and less able children

▣ suggested links to other subject areas within the National Curriculum.

Four photocopiable pages, as follows:
- a pupil worksheet supporting the maths activity
- a pupil worksheet supporting the 'Science link' activity
- a pupil worksheet supporting the science activity
- a supplementary page, which may provide a supporting maths activity for less able children, or a resource or recording sheet for one of the maths or science activities.

Throughout the book, approximate times are given for the activities in both the maths and science lessons. For this age group, the lessons are intended to last a maximum of 60 minutes. However, there are opportunities to lengthen or shorten particular sections to suit your specific needs. In some cases, the lesson may need to be spread over several days, as the children will need to collect results over an extended period of time.

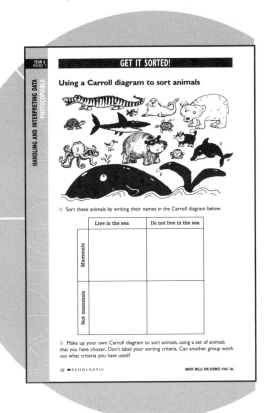

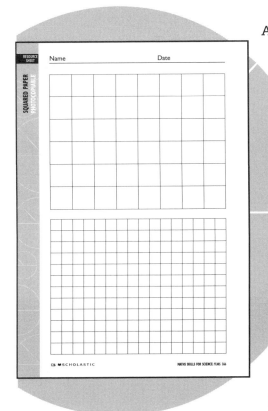

Also included at the back of the book are a number of photocopiable resource pages that can be used with several of the units. Sometimes these are listed with the resources required for individual units, but you might also find them useful in other units – or in other work altogether. These resource pages include a sheet for drawing bar graphs, a sheet for drawing pie charts (divided into 30 equal sections, so that each child in a class of 30 is represented by one section), a sheet with two different sizes of squared paper, a tally chart sheet, and a final 'pupil record sheet'.

This last sheet (which you can photocopy as many times as required) allows the children to make a note of each activity as they complete it, and to record the learning they have gained from it. This record will, in addition, allow you to follow each child's developing maths skills as he or she progresses through Years 5 and 6/Primary 6–7), and help you to identify children who might need particular kinds of support with forthcoming work.

YEAR 5 MATHS SKILLS AND SCIENCE TOPICS

SCIENCE TOPICS / MATHS STRANDS	SOLVING PROBLEMS	MEASURES	SHAPE AND SPACE	RECORDING AND ORGANISING DATA	HANDLING AND INTERPRETING DATA
KEEPING HEALTHY		**Finger on the pulse** Estimating and measuring time. Taking repeated readings of a resting pulse rate.		**How many? How much?** Organising data in tally charts and bar charts. Collecting information about diet and health.	
LIFE CYCLES				**How likely is that?** Considering the probability of different events. Investigating the conditions that affect germination.	
GASES AROUND US	**Choosing the correct calculation** Choosing appropriate number operations to solve problems. Comparing how much air is trapped in different soils.				
CHANGING STATE		**What equipment? What units?** Suggesting and using suitable measuring equipment. Collecting evidence to test a prediction.			**Graphs to show changes** Drawing and interpreting curved line graphs. Obtaining evidence by making careful observations of melting ice.
EARTH, SUN AND MOON			**Which direction?** Recognising positions and directions. The Sun appears to move across the sky.		**What time?** Interpreting and drawing line graphs. Presenting times of sunrise and sunset as a line graph.
CHANGING SOUNDS					**What do you think?** Drawing and interpreting bar charts. Investigating materials that are effective in preventing sound from travelling.
ENQUIRY AND INVESTIGATION				**The truth is out there** Answering a question by collecting, organising and interpreting data. Planning and carrying out a complete investigation.	See above.

YEAR 6 MATHS SKILLS AND SCIENCE TOPICS

MATHS STRANDS ↓ / SCIENCE TOPICS →	INTERDEPENDENCE AND ADAPTATION	MICRO-ORGANISMS	MORE ABOUT DISSOLVING	REVERSIBLE AND IRREVERSIBLE CHANGES	FORCES IN ACTION	HOW WE SEE THINGS	CHANGING CIRCUITS
SOLVING PROBLEMS				**Finding the answers** Choosing appropriate number operations to solve problems. Mixing materials can cause them to change.			
MEASURES		**What proportion?** Measuring and calculating areas. Micro-organisms can cause food to decay.					**How can we measure it?** Suggesting and using suitable units for measuring. The brightness of bulbs in a circuit can be changed.
SHAPE AND SPACE						**What shape is it?** Describing and visualising 3-D shapes. Identifying factors that change a shadow.	
RECORDING AND ORGANISING DATA	**Using pie charts** Interpreting and making pie charts. Fertilisers can be added to soils to provide nutrients for plant growth.				**Making connections** Organising and presenting data. Representing data in a line graph; identifying scientific explanations.		
HANDLING AND INTERPRETING DATA	**Get it sorted!** Drawing and interpreting Carroll diagrams. Looking at ways that plants are suited to their environment.		**Solving and dissolving** Drawing and interpreting line graphs. Planning and carrying out a fair test; drawing a line graph of the results.		**The values in between** Drawing and interpreting line graphs. Presenting data as a line graph and using this to understand forces.		

SOLVING PROBLEMS

CHOOSING THE CORRECT CALCULATION

MATHS FOCUS: SOLVING SINGLE-STEP AND MULTI-STEP PROBLEMS

Learning objectives
■ To choose and use the appropriate number operations to solve problems.
■ To explain and record how a problem was solved.

Resources
■ A board or flip chart and pens.
■ Different-sized small containers, measuring cylinders, rice, pasta, lentils, beads.
■ Copies of photocopiable pages 12 and 13 for each child.

Introduction
10 mins
■ Write a calculation on the board, such as *84 ÷ 14 = 6*. Ask volunteers to make up 'number stories' for this number sentence, such as *If 84cm of liquorice lace is cut into 14cm lengths, 6 children can have a piece each.* Encourage volunteers to draw their number story on the board in pictorial form. Discuss which is easier to understand, the 'picture story' or the original calculation.
■ Extend the number stories with questions, such as *If only 4 children had a piece, how much of the liquorice would be left?* Use a 'picture story' to find the answer.

Whole-class, teacher-directed activity
15–20 mins
■ Write a multi-step problem on the board, such as: *Cans of cat food weigh 400g each. Mr. Patel buys 7 cans of cat food. If Mr Patel can carry 5kg of shopping home, what weight of food will he be able to buy for himself?*
■ Help the children to describe and draw this problem. *What does Mr Patel's shopping bag contain? Who can draw this? How can we draw the food Mr Patel buys for himself? Who can suggest a way to find out how much Mr Patel's food weighs?*
■ Encourage all the children who suggest different methods to explain how they would solve the problem. Help them to draw appropriate pictures and write appropriate number sentences to help other children understand their explanations.

Children's activity
20–25 mins
■ The children should work in pairs to solve the word problems on photocopiable page 12. Encourage them to draw pictures to illustrate each problem, then explain to each other how they can solve it, writing number sentences where appropriate.
■ When they have completed the problems on page 12, encourage them to make up a problem for a friend to solve. The children must be ready to explain how to solve the problem they have set, if this is necessary.

SCIENCE LINK ACTIVITY

Groups of children can use different-sized solid objects (rice, lentils, pasta and beads) to compare two containers of a similar size. Which objects are easier to use? Does it matter whether they are packed neatly or just poured in? The children should draw conclusions, and explain why smaller objects can be used to give a more accurate comparison of the sizes of containers. They can use copies of page 13 for recording.

Differentiation
More able: Encourage these children to work together to invent 'difficult' problems. They must be able to solve their own problems.
Less able: These children can complete the first problem on page 12, and explain to each other how they used pictures to find the solution.

Plenary
10 mins
Look at the methods that different children have used to solve the problems given, and some of the problems they have invented for each other. Emphasise the importance of drawing pictures to help the reader understand what the problem is about.

CHOOSING THE CORRECT CALCULATION

SCIENCE FOCUS: GASES AROUND US (QCA UNIT 5C)

Learning objectives
- To know that soils have air trapped within them.
- To make careful measurements of water volumes.
- To recognise whether measurements need to be repeated.
- To use their results to compare the amounts of air trapped in different soils.

Resources
- Measuring beakers, scoops, hand lenses.
- Three soil samples for each group: dry sand, clay and loam (a mix of sand and clay); water.
- A copy of photocopiable page 14 (page 15 for less able children) for each child .

Safety: Do not collect soil samples from areas that may be contaminated by dog faeces or broken glass. You might prefer to make up your own samples from builder's sand and powdered clay.

Introduction
5–10 mins
- Ask the children: *What living things depend on soil?* They will probably think of plants before animals. Discuss what plants get from soil: anchorage, nutrients and water. *Do any animals depend on soil?* Discuss familiar soil animals such as worms and moles. *What do they get from the soil itself?* They need air, so there must be air in the soil. The type of soil matters too: worms need a soil soft enough to move through, moles need a soil firm enough that tunnels don't collapse.

Whole class, teacher-directed activity
15–20 mins
- Ask: *Are all soils the same?* Discuss any features the children have observed: colour, sandiness, crumbliness and so on. Ask them to examine the soil samples with a hand lens. Discuss what they notice, particularly about the size and shape of the particles.
- Discuss how to compare the amount of air in different soils. If necessary, remind the children that water can be used to 'push' the air out of solids.
- Divide the class into small groups, with some groups using the investigation method on photocopiable page 14 and others using the method on page 15. Discuss the investigation: *How can we make it fair? How can we make the measurements as accurate as possible?* (Stand the beakers on a flat surface to read volumes. Wait until bubbling has stopped before reading. Pour water on very slowly, so you can stop at exactly the 'top of soil' level.)

Children's activity
20–25 mins
- Working in small groups with copies of page 14 or page 15, the children compare the air in the different soil samples. The method given on page 15 is conceptually easier, but the children may need reminding to pour the water very slowly so no bubbles of air are left trapped in the soil.
- When the children have calculated the volume of air in the different soils, ask them to relate this to the size of the particles in each soil type.

Differentiation
More able: The children can use the method on page 14. Ask them to comment on how easy the different soils are to pour or shape. Can they suggest advantages and disadvantages of the soil types for animals living in them?
Less able: The children can use the method on page 15. They may need support in using their results to calculate the volume of air in different soils.

Links to other topics
Science: Relate this work back to QCA Unit 3D (Rocks and soils) by looking at how easily water flows through different types of soil. **Literacy:** Read poems about insects or other small animals. Write poems about an animal of their choice that lives in the soil.

CHOOSING THE CORRECT CALCULATION

Maths in words

■ Solve problem **A** in steps by answering questions **1** to **4** below.

A. Jane waters the 7 school plants. She gives each plant 130ml of water, and her jug holds 250ml. How many times will Jane have to fill up the jug?

1. How much water do all 7 plants need in total? _____

2. One jug holds 250ml. Is this enough? _____

3. If Jane uses 2 jugfuls, how much water is this? _____

Is it enough? _____

4. Keep adding more jugfuls until Jane has enough water. How many jugs does she need in total?

_____

■ Now try these questions.

B. The label on a bottle of fruit squash says 'Dilute 1 part squash with 4 parts water.' If the bottle of undiluted squash holds 750ml, how many ml of diluted squash will the bottle make?

C. At assembly in Mill Lane School hall, the children sit in rows. Each sitting child needs a space 50cm wide and 75cm long. The hall is 8m wide and 12m long. What is the largest number of children that can fit in the hall?

NOW TRY THIS

Make up a problem of your own for your friend to answer. Make sure you can explain how to solve it!

Which container is bigger?

You have been given two containers that are nearly the same size. Can you find out which is the larger container, and how much larger it is?

■ Find out how many large objects, such as beads or cotton reels, fit in each container.

Container A holds

Container B holds

_____   _____

■ Try just dropping the objects into the containers, then packing them in carefully.

Does it make any difference? _____

Which method do you think is best? _____

■ Now fill the containers with very small objects, such as lentils or grains of rice. Use a measuring cylinder to measure how many ml each container holds.

Container A holds

Container B holds

_____   _____

Which container is larger? _____

How much larger is it? _____

NOW TRY THIS

Which method do you think is better for comparing the size of containers? Explain why.

SOLVING PROBLEMS PHOTOCOPIABLE

How much air is in soil?

■ Put 100ml of dry soil into a measuring beaker. Put 100ml of water into a larger measuring beaker.

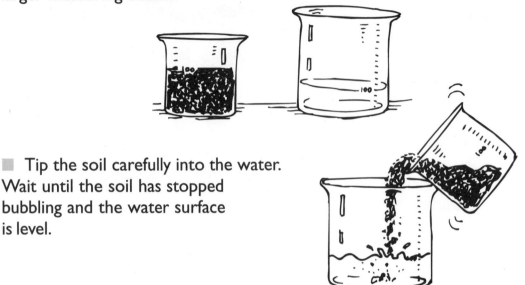

■ Tip the soil carefully into the water. Wait until the soil has stopped bubbling and the water surface is level.

How much has the water level gone up by?
How much of the original 100ml of soil was air?

■ Write your results in the table.

■ Repeat the investigation with a new (dry) sample of the **same type** of soil.

■ Repeat for samples of other types of soil.

Soil type	Water level at start (ml)	Final water level (ml)	Volume of air in soil (ml)
	1st	1st	1st
	2nd	2nd	2nd
	1st	1st	1st
	2nd	2nd	2nd
	1st	1st	1st
	2nd	2nd	2nd

NOW TRY THIS Choose one soil type. Give one advantage and one disadvantage of that soil type for animals living in it.

How much air is in soil?

■ Put 100ml of dry soil into a measuring beaker. Put 100ml of water into a measuring jug.

■ Pour the water **slowly** onto the soil until the water is level with the top of the soil.

How much water is left in the jug?
How much air did the water 'push out' of the soil?

■ Write your results in the table.

■ Repeat your readings with a new (dry) sample of the **same type** of soil.

■ Repeat for samples of other types of soil.

Soil type	Water in jug at start (ml)	Water in jug at end (ml)	Volume of air in soil (ml)
	1st	1st	1st
	2nd	2nd	2nd
	1st	1st	1st
	2nd	2nd	2nd
	1st	1st	1st
	2nd	2nd	2nd

NOW TRY THIS   Choose one soil type. Give one advantage and one disadvantage of that soil type for animals living in it.

WHAT EQUIPMENT? WHAT UNITS?

MATHS FOCUS: USING MEASURING EQUIPMENT

Learning objectives
■ To suggest suitable units and measuring equipment to measure volume, time, area and temperature.
■ To read measuring scales to a suitable degree of accuracy.

Resources
■ A board or flip chart, pens.
■ A range of apparatus to measure volume, length, time and temperature (different-sized measuring jugs, rulers and tape measures, a stopwatch, different clocks, a thermometer); coloured pencils.
■ A copy of photocopiable pages 18 (page 19 for less able children) and 20 for each child.

Introduction
5 mins
■ Ask: *Who can tell me some units to measure length?* Write suggestions on the board, and help the children to identify some lengths that you might use those units for. Check that they know how to use length measurements to find the area of a rectangle. Repeat with units for volume and time.

Whole-class, teacher-directed activity
10–15 mins
■ Show the children a range of measuring equipment. Choose one item. Ask: *What do we use this to measure? What units does it measure in? What are the highest and lowest values it can measure? Can you suggest something that this would be suitable for measuring?* Repeat with some other pieces of measuring equipment.
■ Ask some children to choose the correct piece of measuring equipment to measure values you give them, such as the volume of water in an eggcup or the time taken to run across the playground. Ask them to justify their choice.

Children's activity
20–25 mins
■ Let the children practise reading the scales on a selection of familiar measuring equipment. Ask them to record readings, using appropriate units. They can use photocopiable page 18 to practise choosing the correct units for measuring various lengths, volumes and times, and to draw given values on pictures of measuring equipment. They may find actual examples of values to measure and measuring scales to read helpful. (The answers for page 18 are: **1** min, **2** l, **3** ml, **4** cm, **5** cm², **6** ml, **7** min, **8** m.)

SCIENCE LINK ACTIVITY

This activity will help the children to think about the accuracy of measurements they make, and how they can attempt to improve it. Give them photocopiable page 20 – they have to draw given values on different pieces of apparatus, then use their drawings to decide which apparatus would be best for measuring that value, explaining their choice.

Differentiation
More able: Ask the children to work together, talking about the things that might make a measurement hard to read or inaccurate. Can they suggest ways to make sure their readings are as accurate as possible?
Less able: The children can use photocopiable page 19. (Answers: **1** min, **2** l, **3** cm, **4** ml) Examples of real measuring apparatus using different units may be helpful when they are selecting appropriate units for different values.

Plenary
10 mins
Have a quick-fire question and answer session with questions such as: *What measuring apparatus would you choose to measure...? What units would you use to measure...? What could you measure in...?*

SCIENCE FOCUS: CHANGING STATE (QCA UNIT 5D)

Learning objectives
- To express ideas in a form that can be investigated.
- To make a prediction and decide what evidence to collect.
- To make careful measurements, recording them in tables and/or bar graphs.
- To identify trends in results and to use these to draw conclusions, indicating whether the results support the prediction.

Resources
- Suitable apparatus for measuring small volumes of water.
- Paper towels, pegs, string, stopwatches, a battery-powered fan.
- Access to places at different temperatures.
- A copy of photocopiable page 21, and resource page 126 (or graph paper for more able children) for each child.

Introduction
5–10 mins
- Recap the children's knowledge of evaporation. Ask: *Who can describe some places where evaporation happens? Do things always evaporate at the same rate?* Ask the children to suggest factors that affect how quickly water evaporates from a damp paper towel. Make a list. This should include temperature, area (how folded the towel is), the amount of water on the towel and whether the towel is in a draught.

Whole-class, teacher-directed activity
10–15 mins
- Help the children to express their ideas about what factors affect evaporation in the form of questions that can be investigated, such as: *Does the temperature affect how quickly water evaporates?* Make a new list of these questions.
- For each of the questions on your list, help a group to plan an investigation to find the answer. Consider what needs to be changed, what needs to be measured, and how the test can be kept fair.
- Tell the children that each group will have to find ways of making their results as accurate as possible. Discuss some of the possible ways, such as: choosing measuring apparatus with appropriate scales; getting a second person to check the first person's reading; repeating readings (if time allows).
- Discuss possible ways to present the results: in tables, in a bar chart, or even (for more able children) as a line graph.

Children's activity
20–25 mins
- Each group should choose one factor that might affect the time a damp paper towel takes to dry. They should make a prediction about the effect that their factor will have, then plan an investigation to test it. They will need to consider: what to change; what to keep the same (to make it a fair test), how often to check the towel; how to decide when the towel is dry; and how to record and present their results. They can use photocopiable page 21 to help them plan and record the investigation.

Differentiation
More able: Encourage the children to investigate a factor that allows for several readings, such as area (measure against squared paper) or temperature. Encourage them to present their results as a line graph of time taken to dry against either area or temperature.
Less able: Encourage these children to use only two or three values of the factor they are changing (such as windy/not windy, hot/warm/cold or spread out/folded up), and simply to decide which towel dries first.

Links to other topics
Geography: Why crops often have to be irrigated (watered) when grown in hot countries.
Design and technology: Design an efficient clothes drier.

WHAT EQUIPMENT? WHAT UNITS?

Units and measuring

■ Choose the correct unit from the box to measure each of the things listed below. Each unit may be used once, more than once or not at all. You may even need units that are not listed!

m	ml	h	mm
l	min	cm	s

1. The time taken for a bath to fill. _____

2. The volume of water in a bath. _____

3. The volume of tea in a mug. _____

4. The width of a sheet of paper. _____

5. The area of a sheet of paper. _____

6. The volume of medicine in a dose. _____

7. The time a swimming costume takes to dry in summer. _____

8. The distance you can run. _____

Complete these drawings of measuring instruments so they read the values shown.

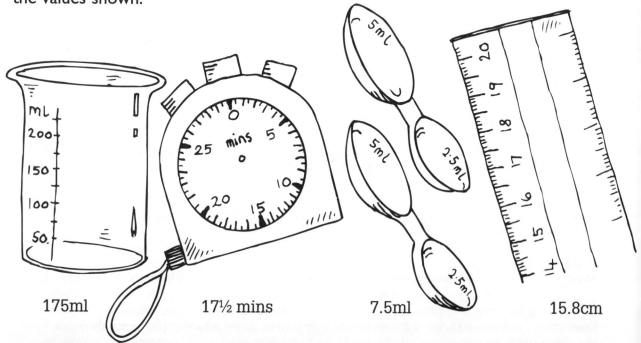

175ml   17½ mins   7.5ml   15.8cm

NOW TRY THIS Suggest some things that might make our measurements of volumes, lengths or times inaccurate.

MATHS SKILLS FOR SCIENCE: YEARS 5&6

Units to measure

■ Circle the correct unit to measure each of these things.

1. A bath would take seconds/minutes/metres to fill.

2. A bath would hold metres/litres of water.

3. A sheet of writing paper would be minutes/centimetres/metres wide.

4. There would be millimetres/millilitres of medicine in one dose.

■ Write the correct unit in short form (mm, l, min and so on) next to each of the above statements.

■ Match each of these pictures of measuring apparatus to the unit it would use.

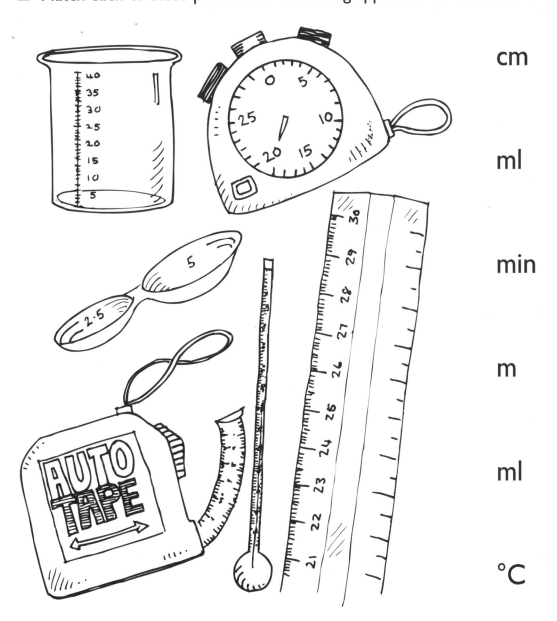

cm

ml

min

m

ml

°C

WHAT EQUIPMENT? WHAT UNITS?

Choosing the most accurate instrument

◼ Draw 10ml of water in each of these measuring beakers.

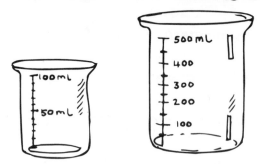

Which would you choose to measure 10ml? Why?

_____

_____

◼ Draw a temperature of 37.5°C on each of these thermometers.

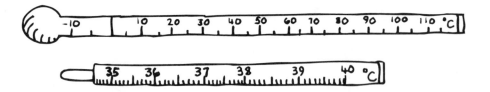

Which would you choose to measure 37.5°C? Why?

_____

_____

◼ Draw a time of 6s on each of these stopwatches.

Which would you choose to measure 6s? Why?

_____

_____

NOW TRY THIS

Suggest values that you might choose to measure with the other instruments.

WHAT EQUIPMENT? WHAT UNITS?

Investigating how quickly paper towels dry

What question will you investigate?

____

____

- Draw how you set up your investigation.

How will you make sure it is a fair test?

____

____

- Use this space to record your results.

Which towel dried most quickly? ________________________

What have you learned from your investigation?

____

____

NOW TRY THIS

Plot your results as a line graph.
What does your graph tell you?

MEASURES

FINGER ON THE PULSE

MATHS FOCUS: MEASURING AND ESTIMATING TIME

Learning objectives
- To read stopwatches accurately.
- To suggest and use suitable units for measuring different times.
- To estimate and measure the times taken by different events.

Resources
- Stopwatches, a large drawing or cardboard cut-out of a stopwatch.
- A copy of photocopiable pages 24, 25 and 26, and resource page 124 for each child.

Introduction
5 mins
- Discuss situations where children need to read written times (bus timetables, TV listings, recipes) and situations where they need to use a watch or other timer (a race, catching a train, cooking).

Whole-class, teacher-directed activity
20–25 mins
- Practise reading the time on a stopwatch. Use a drawing or cardboard cut-out of a stopwatch like those at your school (either analogue or digital). Show different times on this stopwatch and ask the children to read them. Ask them to show you the display for a time of 1 minute, 1 minute 20 seconds, and so on.
- Ask the children to suggest suitable units to measure different times: journey to school, time of darkness at night, time to run across the playground, age of a person, time to read a library book and so on.

Children's activity
20–25 mins
- Ask pairs or small groups to practise using a stopwatch to time a variety of activities, such as running across the playground or reading a poem. For each activity, they should measure and record three times and then decide which they think is the most accurate time.
- The children then take turns to estimate one minute, while another child uses a hidden stopwatch to time their estimate. They should record their estimates and, if time allows, try again to see whether their second estimate is more accurate.
- Photocopiable pages 24 and 25 can be used to record the results of both parts of the activity.

Differentiation
More able: Ask the children to work out an average time for each activity from the three times they have measured.
Less able: The children can be encouraged to see the middle reading of their three times as the 'most accurate'. For some activities, such as running across the playground, they may choose another value: 'The first reading was the most accurate, because the other two times she was tired.'

SCIENCE LINK ACTIVITY

The children make a class tally chart to show the number of seconds they estimated to be a minute (use their first estimate from the children's activity above). They can use photocopiable page 26 to group the times into 10-second 'batches' and then use resource page 124 to plot a bar chart of this grouped data, showing how many children estimated each 'batch' of times.

Plenary
10 mins
Discuss how accurate the children think their timings were, and factors that might affect the accuracy of a reading of time. *Longer times are more accurate, because it does not matter so much if you do not start the stopwatch at exactly the right time. Taking three readings is more accurate than taking one, because you can see if one reading is different from the other two and check it again.*

SCIENCE FOCUS: KEEPING HEALTHY (QCA UNIT 5A)

Learning objectives
- To measure pulse rate and relate it to heartbeat.
- To take repeat readings of the resting pulse rate.
- To make a bar chart for grouped data.

Resources
- Stopwatches or timers accurate to 1 minute.
- A copy for each child of photocopiable page 27 and resource page 124, an A3 copy of resource page 127.

Safety: The children should undertake physical activities for long enough to notice changes such as becoming tired, warm or out of breath, but not long enough to become overtired. These are normal PE activities only, not endurance tests!

Introduction
10 mins
- Show the children where they can feel their pulse (wrist or neck). Let them practise finding and feeling the pulse. Show them how doctors and nurses feel the pulse in the wrist, using two fingers (with the thumb below the wrist).
- Discuss what the pulse is. Relate this to the pump action of the heart. Explain that a pulse is felt at points where the arteries are close to the surface.

Whole-class, teacher-directed activity
20 mins
- Ask the children to find and count their pulse while you time for 1 minute. Tell them to remember the value. Ask: *Do you think our pulse rate ever changes? Do you think our heartbeat changes?*
- Ask the children to jump up and down, run on the spot and so on. Discuss the changes they notice, including changes in the pulse rate.
- Ask: *Do you think we all have the same pulse rate?* Discuss what this means, and how to make a fair comparison. For example, it would not be a fair comparison to measure the pulse for one person resting and another person running.
- Tell the children that they are going to compare resting pulse rates for the whole class. Discuss the importance of taking repeat readings, how to choose the most accurate reading, and how to record on a class tally chart (A3 copy of resource page 127). Label the chart with appropriate groupings of pulse rate, and make sure the children know how to decide which group to put their reading into. (Appropriate groupings might be 60–64, 65–69 and so on up to 105–109).

Children's activity
20–25 mins
- The children work in small groups to take three readings of their resting pulse rate and record these on photocopiable page 27. Some children may prefer to time for 30 seconds and double, others may find timing for 1 minute easier. They should decide which value is the most accurate (usually the middle value) and contribute this value to the class tally chart.
- The children use the class tally chart to plot a bar graph on resource page 124, showing the grouped values of pulse rate and the number of children in each group. They can use this graph to answer the questions on page 27.

Differentiation
More able: Ask the children to contribute an average value of their pulse rate readings to the class tally chart.
Less able: Provide the children with a copy of resource page 124 with the axes already labelled.

Links to other topics
Literacy: Descriptive writing – write a story involving action, describing exactly how someone feels after exercise.
Music: Compose some music in which the sound of a beat (like a heartbeat) is important.

FINGER ON THE PULSE

How long did it take?

▩ Choose an activity to time. Measure how long it takes you. Record the result in the first table on your recording sheet.

▩ Now time everyone in your group. Record their times on the 'Recording sheet'. Repeat until you have 3 times for each person in your group.

▩ Decide which is the most accurate time for each person. Record it in the table.

▩ Choose two more activities to time. Find accurate times for everyone in your group, as before. Record the results in the second table on your recording sheet.

▩ Ask one person in your group to shut their eyes and estimate when 1 minute is up.

▩ Time their estimate. Record the time in the table below. Repeat for everyone in your group.

▩ If you have time, record a second estimate of 1 minute for everyone in your group. Was it more accurate than their first estimate?

Name	1st estimate of 1 minute	2nd estimate of 1 minute

MEASURES
PHOTOCOPIABLE

How long did it take? – recording sheet

Activity: _____

Name	1st time	2nd time	3rd time	Most accurate time

Activity: _____

Name	1st time	2nd time	3rd time	Most accurate time

Activity: _____

Name	1st time	2nd time	3rd time	Most accurate time

FINGER ON THE PULSE

Just a minute

■ Use your class tally chart to fill in this table, showing how much time the children in your class estimated 1 minute to be.

Time estimated to be 1 minute	Number of children
0–10 seconds	
10–20 seconds	
20–30 seconds	
30–40 seconds	
40–50 seconds	
50–60 seconds	
60–70 seconds	
70–80 seconds	
80–90 seconds	
More than 90 seconds	

■ Plot a bar chart to show the number of children whose estimates were in each group of times.

Which was the most common estimate? _____

An accurate estimate of 1 minute would be within the nearest 10 seconds.

How many of the children were this accurate? _____

NOW TRY THIS How do you think the bar chart would change if you plotted the children's second estimate of 1 minute?

Measuring pulse rate

■ Measure the resting pulse rate of the children in your group. Record your measurements in this table.

Name	1st reading	2nd reading	3rd reading	Most accurate pulse rate

■ Record the most accurate value of each child's pulse rate on your class tally chart.

■ Use the totals on your class tally chart to plot a bar chart showing the number of children with pulse rates in each range of values.

Which was the most common range of pulse rates?

_____

What was the fastest range of pulse rates? _____

How many children were in this group? _____

What was the slowest range of pulse rates? _____

How many children were in this group? _____

SHAPE AND SPACE

WHICH DIRECTION?

MATHS FOCUS: RECOGNISING POSITIONS AND DIRECTIONS

Learning objectives
- Recognise positions and directions.
- Use the eight compass directions N, NE, E, SE, S, SW, W, NW.

Resources
- Metre rulers.
- A copy of photocopiable pages 30 (page 31 for less able children) and 32 for each child.

Introduction
5 mins
- Tell the children: *Today we are going to think about different ways to record information and how helpful they are to other people.* Ask them what information they would need to record in order to tell someone about the classroom. *What are the most important/large/ noticeable objects in our classroom? How can we describe where these objects are?*

Whole-class, teacher-directed activity
20–25 mins
- Ask the children to sit at their desks and imagine they are describing where things are in the classroom, using distances and directions. *Is it enough to tell someone just the distance or the direction to an object, or do they need to know both? Why?*
- Ask individual children to describe the positions of some objects, using distances and directions: *It's about 3m in front of me. It's about 2m to my right,* and so on.
- Ask other children to describe the positions of the same objects. Point out that for some an object will be to the left, for others it will be to the right. Explain that for someone else to picture the classroom, all the objects must be described from the same starting point.
- Show the children a copy of photocopiable page 30 and make sure they all understand the directions used on the sheet. It might be helpful to put up signs saying *front, back, left* and *right* on the appropriate classroom walls, or on an object such as a toy animal or train.

Children's activity
20–25 mins
- The children work in pairs to plot five classroom objects of their choice on the plan on page 30. Each pair should draw their own table in the centre of the page, then use a scale of either 1cm = 1m or 2cm = 1m (you decide which will fit better for your classroom) to draw other objects. For each object they must decide which direction it is in and measure how far away it is before transferring this information to their plan.

SCIENCE LINK ACTIVITY

Photocopiable page 32 shows a treasure map. The children play 'Hunt the treasure' in pairs. Each child decides on secret locations for four different objects. His or her partner then asks questions to find the direction and distance of each 'buried' object from the central palm tree.

Differentiation
More able: Encourage the children to estimate the approximate angle between a line to their chosen object and the 'straight forward' or 'straight backwards' line, then draw approximately the same angle on their plan.
Less able: The children can use photocopiable page 31, finding three objects approximately 1m, 2m and 3m away from their table and deciding which section of the 'classroom plan' these objects belong in.

Plenary
10 mins
Look together at the plans some pairs of children have drawn. Help them to see that these plans are all the same, but are shifted to the left or right and the front or back depending on where different pairs were sitting.

SCIENCE FOCUS: EARTH, SUN AND MOON (QCA UNIT 5E)

Learning objectives
- To know that the Sun appears to move across the sky in the course of a day.
- To understand that evidence may be interpreted in more than one way.

Resources
- Playground chalk, a compass, metre rulers, a torch, a pencil.
- Straight sticks held upright in plant pots of sand.
- A copy of photocopiable page 33 for each child.

Introduction
5–10 mins
- Discuss the children's experience of shadows cast by the Sun. Check they all know that the position of a shadow can move. Demonstrate this with a torch and a pencil, if necessary. Question the children about shadows: *Where will your shadow be if the Sun is over here? Where is the Sun if your shadow is in this direction?*

Whole-class, teacher-directed activity
20 mins
- Ask: *Does the Sun shine from the same direction all day?* Discuss where the Sun shines into the school, or their homes, at different times of the day. Ask the children what this tells them about the Sun. *Does the Sun really move across the sky?* Make sure they understand that the Earth is turning and the Sun is not moving around the Earth.
- Ask the children to predict what will happen to the shadow of a stick set upright in a sunny part of the playground. *What direction will it move in?*
- Show the children the plan on photocopiable page 33. Mark the four main compass directions on the playground, and show the children how we can use these to determine what direction a shadow is pointing in. Make sure all the children understand how to record a shadow as a line on their chart, pointing in the right direction and with a label to show the length of the real shadow.

Children's activity
20–25 mins
- Working in small groups, the children set up a stick in a sunny part of the playground where it won't be disturbed. They can mark the four main compass directions at the base of the stick if they wish. Then, every hour throughout a school day, they measure the length and direction of the shadow and record both on the plan on page 33. They should record the time next to each line they draw.
- They can now use their plan to predict the length and direction of the shadow at times when they have not measured it, and to estimate the time when the shadow would be pointing south. (The shadow would point south in the middle of the night. We won't see this because the Earth is blocking the Sun's light.)

Differentiation
More able: Ask the children to use the changing position of the shadow to work out the direction of the Sun's apparent movement during the day. They can use a torch and pencil to model this movement.
Less able: The children can use chalk to draw the shadow on the playground at different times and label each shadow with the time. They can then use this record to predict the length and direction of the shadow at unmeasured times.

Links to other topics
Literacy/Drama: Myths, legends and stories from different cultures to explain why the Sun and Moon move in the sky. **Art:** Illustrating Sun and Moon legends.

SHAPE AND SPACE

WHICH DIRECTION?

Making a classroom plan

■ Draw your table at the centre of the classroom plan below.

■ Choose one object in your classroom.
  ■ How far is it from your table?
  ■ Which direction is it in?

■ Draw the object in the correct place on your plan.

■ Repeat for four more objects.

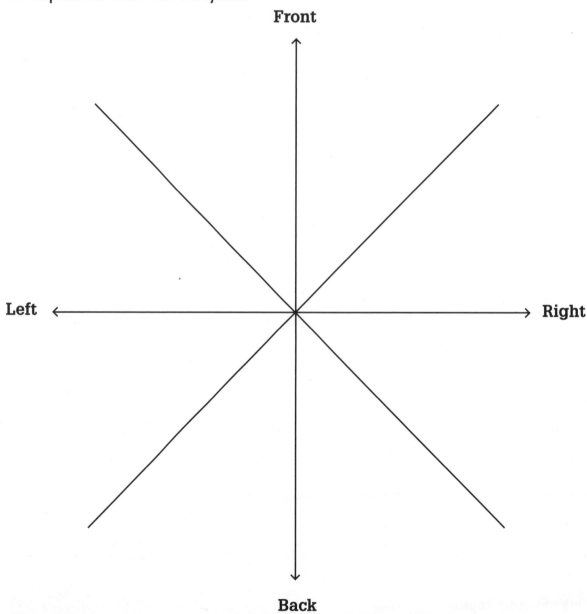

Front

Left

Right

Back

NOW TRY THIS Can you estimate the angle between the 'straight forward' line (the line pointing to the front) and the line to one of your objects?

Making a classroom plan

▨ Draw your table at the centre of the classroom plan below.

▨ Find an object that is about 1m away from your table.
  ▪ Which direction is it in?

▨ Draw the object in the correct place on your plan.

▨ Repeat for objects that are about 2m and 3m from your table.

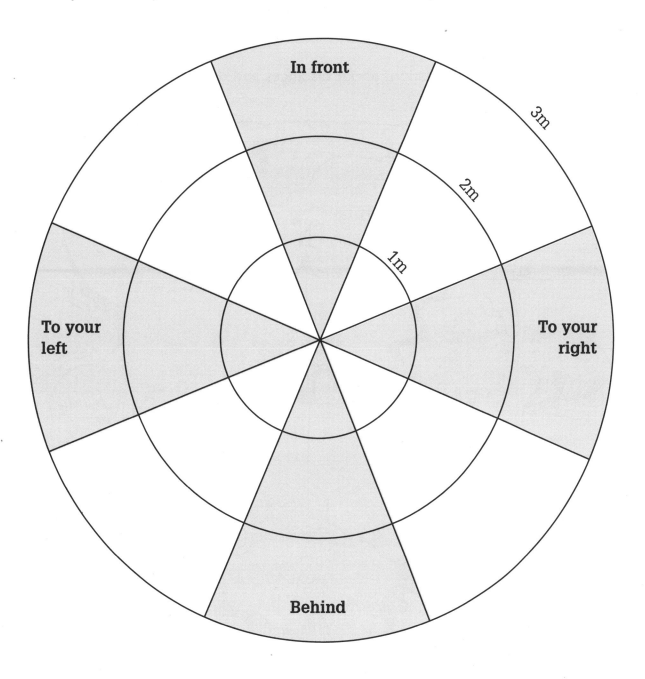

Find the treasure

■ Look at this map of Turtle Island.

■ Mark the following items of buried treasure on the island:
  ■ a chest of gold pieces (mark with G)
  ■ a diamond ring (mark with D)
  ■ a silver sword (mark with S)
  ■ a telescope (mark with T).

■ For each item of treasure, record its distance and direction from the palm trees in the middle of the island.

Can your partner ask questions about distances and directions to find all of your buried treasure?

Telling the time with shadows

▨ Mark the length and direction of your stick's shadow at 9:00am, then every hour for the rest of the day.

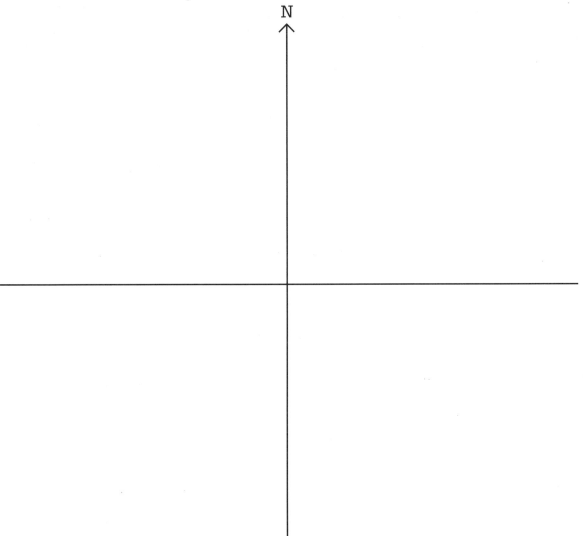

▨ Use this plan to find the length and direction of the shadow at 2:30pm. Draw this shadow on the plan.

Length of shadow: _____

When do you think your shadow would point south?

_____

_____

Why won't you see a shadow pointing south?

_____

_____

RECORDING AND ORGANISING DATA

HOW LIKELY IS THAT?

MATHS FOCUS: CONSIDERING THE PROBABILITY OF DIFFERENT EVENTS

Learning objectives
- To use the language associated with probability to discuss events.
- To put events in the correct position on a probability scale.

Resources
- A board or flip chart, pens.
- A large dice, a coin, a pack of playing cards, a selection of coloured cubes, scissors, adhesive.
- A copy of photocopiable pages 36, 37 and 38 for each child.

Introduction
5 mins
- Tell the children: *We are going to think about how likely some events are. What do I mean if I say something is 'likely to happen'? What about if it is 'unlikely'?* Ask the children for examples of events that are likely or unlikely. Do the other children agree?

Whole-class, teacher-directed activity
20 mins
- Draw a probability scale on the board in the form of a strip labelled 'unlikely' at the left-hand end and 'likely' at the right-hand end. Ask: *Who can think of something that is certain to happen? Where should we put it on the scale?* Mark it in the correct place. Repeat with things that definitely won't happen, are 'quite likely' and are 'quite unlikely', asking volunteers to mark them in the correct places.
- Introduce the use of the word *chance* to describe how likely an event is. Help the children to put the words *certain, no chance, poor chance, good chance* and *even chance* in the correct places on the probability scale (see below). Discuss what an 'even chance' means.
- Show the children the dice, playing cards, coin and blocks or beads. Make statements such as *The coin is quite likely to land on its side. I have an even chance of rolling an odd number. If I select a bead at random, it is certain to be blue.* Challenge the children to decide whether each statement is true or false and, if it is false, to make up a true statement.

no chance	poor chance	even chance	good chance	certain

Children's activity
20–25 mins
- The children work in pairs to discuss the statements on photocopiable page 36, deciding where to place them on a probability scale. They should cut out the sections from page 37 and use them to make a probability scale, then write the statements in the correct places. They should then make up other statements of their own and place them on the scale.

Differentiation
More able: Challenge the children to suggest changes they could make to two of the statements on page 36 to make them either more or less likely.

Less able: The children should work together to find just two 'likely' and two 'unlikely' statements on page 36.

SCIENCE LINK ACTIVITY

The children work together, using photocopiable page 38 and their knowledge of plant growth, to decide how likely different plants are to grow in different conditions, showing their answers on a probability scale.

Plenary
10 mins
Discuss how we decide how likely something is. Encourage suggestions that have to do with how many times an event happens compared with other events, such as *I've seen lots of goals but I've never seen the ball balance on the crossbar, so I think it's very unlikely* or *The potatoes in a school dinner are chips about half the time, so I think it's an even chance.* These ideas will form the basis of more advanced probability work in later years.

SCIENCE FOCUS: LIFE CYCLES (QCA UNIT 5B)

Learning objectives
- To consider conditions that might affect germination and plan how to test them.
- To plan how to alter one factor at a time in order to carry out a fair test.
- To know that seeds need warmth and water, but not light, for germination.

Resources
- Shallow trays lined with kitchen towel or cotton wool.
- Fast-growing seeds such as cress or mung beans.
- A copy of photocopiable page 39 and a class probability scale (enlarged copy of page 37) for each child.

Introduction
5–10 mins
- Recap on the conditions necessary for healthy plant growth. The children should know that plants need water, warmth and light. Soil is not essential, though it provides anchorage and some nutrients. Ask the children what conditions seeds might need to germinate. List their ideas.

Whole-class, teacher-directed activity
15–20 mins
- Ask: *How could we investigate the conditions that seeds need to germinate?* Identify water, warmth and light as possible factors to investigate, since these affect plant growth. *What should we change and what should we keep the same?* Establish that for a fair test only one factor at a time can be changed.
- Divide the children into groups, with at least two groups investigating each of the three factors. Ask the children to describe what they will do, what they will measure and how they will use their measurements to decide which seeds have germinated best. (The simplest and most reliable method is to plant roughly equal numbers of seeds in each tray and record the number of seeds that have germinated after a week.) Each group should use seeds in three different conditions: very wet, moist and dry; cold, warm and hot; or dark, gloomy and bright.

Children's activity
25–30 mins
- Working in groups, the children set up three trays of seeds, varying the factor they are investigating and choosing what they consider to be optimum values for the other factors. They should use photocopiable page 39 to record how they set up the investigation, approximately how many seeds they have planted and their prediction of which seeds will germinate best.
- After one week, they should record how many seeds have germinated in each tray. They should then place labels (such as *cold, warm* and *hot*) on a class probability scale to show how likely they think seeds are to germinate in each of the conditions they have investigated.
- In a plenary session, look at the class probability scale and deduce the conditions of light, warmth and water in which seeds are most likely to germinate.

Differentiation
More able: Ask the children to evaluate how good this method is at determining the conditions needed for germination. Can they suggest any improvements?
Less able: The children may need help with converting the numbers of germinated seeds into positions on a probability scale. For example, if half the seeds in a sample germinated, the probability of a seed germinating in those conditions is ½.

Links to other topics
Literacy: Write sowing or growing instructions for a packet of seeds (keep it brief – there's not much room on a seed packet).

HOW LIKELY IS THAT?

Likely and unlikely

◼ Cut out the strips on your 'Probability scale' sheet. Glue them together to make your own probability scale.

◼ Discuss the statements below. Decide how likely each statement is. What is the chance that it will happen?

◼ Cut out these statements and stick them in the correct places on your probability scale.

◼ Make up some more statements. Write them in the correct places on your probability scale.

We will do maths today.	It will rain today.	We will have a meal at lunchtime today.
If I roll a dice, I will roll an even number.	An escaped lion will run into our playground.	We will have a test this afternoon.
Our headteacher will come into our class to visit us.	Our teacher will choose a girl to answer the next question.	William the Conqueror will visit us.

NOW TRY THIS   Discuss how you could change two of the statements you have cut out to make them either more likely or less likely.

Probability scale

Glue here	Glue here	
Poor chance		Certain
	Even chance	
No chance		Good chance

HOW LIKELY IS THAT?

Plants in the classroom

The children in Class 5 had to look after these three plants for two weeks.

Cactus

House plant

Young seedling

"What if we forget to water them?" asked Katie.

▨ Draw a probability scale with the title 'No water'. Then draw each plant in the correct place to show how likely it is to survive.

"What if we leave them too close to the radiator?" asked Henry.

▨ Draw a probability scale with the title 'Very hot'. Then draw each plant in the correct place to show how likely it is to survive.

Which plant do you think Class 5 will find easiest to look after? Why?

_____

_____

_____

When do seeds germinate best?

What are you going to investigate?

_____

_____

■ Explain **briefly** how you will carry out your investigation.

_____

_____

_____

_____

How many seeds will you use in each tray? _____

■ Leave your seeds for one week, then count how many seeds have germinated. Record the results in this table.

Condition the seeds were planted in	How many seeds germinated

■ Use your results to help you decide how likely seeds are to germinate in each of the conditions you tested. Write the three conditions in the correct places on your class probability scale.

■ What do you think are the best conditions for helping seeds to germinate? Use your class probability scale to explain why.

_____

_____

RECORDING AND ORGANISING DATA

HOW MANY? HOW MUCH?

MATHS FOCUS: ORGANISING DATA IN TALLY CHARTS AND BAR CHARTS

Learning objectives
- To solve a problem by collecting data and representing it in a tally chart and a bar chart.
- To begin to use simple pie charts.

Resources
- A board or flip chart, pens, rulers, coloured pencils, scrap paper.
- A copy of photocopiable pages 42 (page 43 for less able children) and 44, and of resource pages 124, 125 and 127 for each child; A3 copies of resource pages 124 (one copy), 125 (one copy) and 127 (two copies).

Introduction
5–10 mins
- Give the children a small piece of scrap paper. Ask them to secretly write down a number from 1 to 10. Ask: *Which number did the most children write? What were the highest and lowest numbers? How many children chose 3?* Write these questions on the board. Ask the children how they could find the answers. Prompt them to think about tally and bar charts.

Whole-class, teacher-directed activity
15–20 mins
- Using an A3 copy of resource page 127, work together to make a class tally chart of the numbers the children chose. Use an A3 copy of resource page 124 to make a bar chart from this information. Use the bar chart to find the answers to your original questions.
- Introduce, or reintroduce, the terms *mode* (the value that occurred most often) and *range* (the difference between the highest and lowest values).
- If appropriate, show the children how to make a simple pie chart from their data, using an A3 copy of resource page 125. (Use one section for each child in your class; invent or miss out results as necessary to make 30 results.) Colour the sections as appropriate, using a different colour for each number and putting all the same-coloured sections together. Discuss what the pie chart shows, using only simple fractions such as 'less than a quarter', 'nearly a third'. Do not attempt to find out anything more complex from the pie chart at this stage.

Children's activity
25–30 mins
- On another A3 copy of resource page 127, make a class tally chart of the number of TV programmes the children watched the previous day. Working in pairs, the children should use this information to complete photocopiable page 42 and then plot a bar graph, using resource page xx1, to show how many children watched different numbers of programmes. They can now find the mode and the range.
- Children completing this quickly can use resource page 125 to plot a rough pie chart of the numbers of children watching different numbers of programmes, rounding the values to simple fractions ('nearly ¼ watched 3 programmes').

SCIENCE LINK ACTIVITY
The children use the data provided on photocopiable page 44 to make a pie chart on resource page 125. Each group should decide on a key for the pie chart. Alternatively, the children could be asked to present the data as a bar graph.

Differentiation
More able: The children can work in pairs, using resource page 125 to make an accurate pie chart of the numbers of children watching different numbers of programmes. (They can omit or add results.)
Less able: The children should use photocopiable page 43 to make a bar chart presenting the information for the children in their group.

Plenary
10 mins
Recap on how to make a bar chart from a tally chart, and what the mode and range are. Encourage the children to explain how they found the mode and range.

SCIENCE FOCUS: KEEPING HEALTHY (QCA UNIT 5A)

Learning objectives
- To know that we need an adequate and varied diet to stay healthy.
- To collect information about diet and health.

Resources
- Pictures or examples of a wide variety of foods or food packages, including some from all the main food groups (see below).
- A copy of photocopiable page 45 and resource page 124 for each child; a class tally chart (A3 copy of resource page 124).

Preparation: Before this lesson, ask the children to record all the food they eat for one day. (This could be a homework activity.)

Introduction
5–10 mins
- Ask the children what they understand by *diet*. Discuss their ideas. Establish the idea that the term 'diet' describes all the different types of food that we eat. Our food is divided into several 'food groups', which provide different things that we need. Ask: *Can you name any of the main food groups?* The children may remember work they have done on 'food for growth' and 'food for activity'.

Whole-class, teacher-directed activity
15–20 mins
- Show the children the selection of foods or food packages. Help them to identify examples of foods belonging to all the main food groups: fats and oils; sugars and starches; proteins; vitamins and minerals; and fibre. Discuss why it is important to eat a varied diet, including foods from all the different groups.
- Tell the children that experts on diet say we should eat five helpings of fruit or vegetables every day. Discuss some of the foods that can be counted as fruit or vegetables, such as fruit juice, tinned fruit or frozen vegetables.
- Ask: *How could we record the number of helpings of fruit and vegetables that the children in our class eat?* If necessary, remind them about using a bar graph (and a pie chart, if they have experienced this) to show the frequency of different events.

Children's activity
20–25 mins
- Ask the children to identify how many helpings of fruit or vegetables they ate the previous day. (A standard helping might be, for example, one medium-sized piece of fruit, ½ cup of cooked peas or beans, ½ cup of raw non-leafy vegetables, 1 cup of raw leafy vegetables.) Record each child's number of helpings on a class tally chart with the rows labelled '0 helpings', '1 helping' and so on. Display this prominently (or photocopy it for each group).
- The children should plot a bar graph on a copy of resource page 124, using photocopiable page 45 to help them draw up a table of the class data. They can use their bar graph to answer the questions about mode and range on photocopiable page 45.
- Use discussion to relate the children's answers to what they know about healthy eating. Ask each group to produce a poster, leaflet or menu encouraging other children to eat more fruit and vegetables.

Differentiation
More able: The children can discuss the extension question on page 45 in groups.
Less able: Help the children to transfer the information on the class tally chart to the table on photocopiable page 45. They could produce a block graph instead of a bar graph.

Links to other topics
ICT: Use software packages on the computer to present data in the form of bar graphs or pie charts.

HOW MANY? HOW MUCH?

How many TV programmes do we watch?

▨ Use the information from the class tally chart to complete this table.

Number of television programmes watched	Number of children
0	
1	
2	
3	
4	
5	

▨ Show this information in a bar graph, using the sheet you have been given.

▨ Complete these sentences.

1. The _____ is the number of TV programmes watched by the biggest number of children.

2. The **range** is the difference between the _____ number of programmes watched and the lowest number of programmes watched by any child.

▨ Answer these questions.

1. What was the lowest number of TV programmes watched? _____

2. What was the highest number of TV programmes watched? _____

3. What was the range? _____

4. What was the mode? _____

NOW TRY THIS Can you use the pie chart sheet to show the number of TV programmes watched by the children as a pie chart?

Making a bar graph

▨ Fill in the table to show how many television programmes the children in your group watched.

Number of television programmes watched	Number of children
0	
1	
2	
3	
4	

▨ Label your bar graph sheet like this.

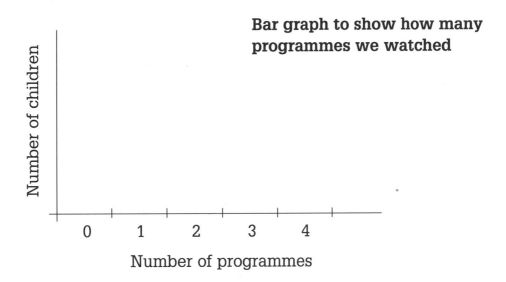

Bar graph to show how many programmes we watched

How many children watched no TV programmes? _____

▨ Fill in that many squares in the first column of your bar graph.

▨ Do the same for the other numbers of TV programmes.

How many TV programmes did the biggest number of children watch? _____
This is called the **mode**.

HOW MANY? HOW MUCH?

Fruit and vegetable pie chart

The children in Class 5 made a tally chart to show how many helpings of fruit and vegetables they had eaten.

Here are their results:

Number of helpings	How many children	Total
1	|	
2	||	
3	ⅢⅢ ||||	
4	ⅢⅢ ⅢⅢ |	
5	ⅢⅢ	
6 or more	||	

▨ Fill in the 'Total' column.

▨ Draw a key on your pie chart sheet, using different colours for '1 helping', '2 helpings' and so on.

▨ For each child who had 1 helping of fruit and vegetables, fill in 1 section of the pie chart with your '1 helping' colour.

▨ Repeat for the other numbers of helpings.

What proportion (approximately) of the children ate 3 helpings of fruit or vegetables?

_____

Experts on diet say we should eat 5 helpings of fruit and vegetables each day. Approximately what proportion of the children in Class 5 eat the right amount of fruit and vegetables?

_____

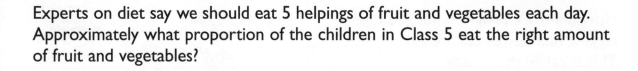

HOW MANY? HOW MUCH?

RECORDING AND ORGANISING DATA

PHOTOCOPIABLE

How healthy is our diet?

■ Use the information from your class tally chart to fill in this table.

How many helpings	How many children

■ Use the bar graph sheet to show the information as a bar chart.

■ Answer these questions.

1. What was the smallest number of helpings eaten? _____

2. What was the largest number of helpings eaten? _____

3. What was the range? _____

4. What was the most common number of helpings? _____

5. What is this number called? _____

6. How many children ate this number of helpings? _____

NOW TRY THIS

Discuss how you could find out what types of fruit and vegetables are most popular with the children in your class.

GRAPHS TO SHOW CHANGES

HANDLING AND INTERPRETING DATA

MATHS FOCUS: DRAWING AND INTERPRETING CURVED LINE GRAPHS

Learning objectives
■ To draw and interpret a line graph.
■ To understand that intermediate points on a line graph may have meaning.

Resources
■ A board or flip chart, pens.
■ Graph paper, rulers.
■ A copy of photocopiable pages 48 and 49 and resource page 126 for each child.

Introduction
5 mins
■ Recap on the main features of a line graph: a title, two labelled axes with units. Ask the children why each of these is important. Discuss some things a line graph could be used to show, and what axes these graphs would need.

Whole-class, teacher-directed activity
20–25 mins
■ Draw a straight-line graph of temperature increasing with time. Ask the children to explain what this shows. Draw a straight-line graph of temperature decreasing with time. Help the children to explain what this shows.

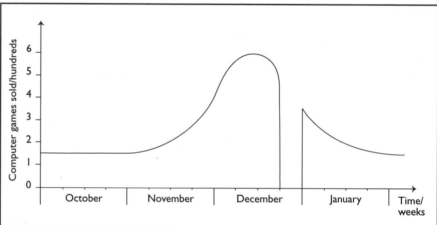

■ Copy the graph shown on the right onto the board. (It does not have to be an exact copy: the general shape is what matters.) Make sure the children understand the labels on the axes.
■ Discuss the shape of the graph with the children. *When does the number of computer games sold remain the same? When is the number increasing? When is it decreasing?* Discuss when the number is changing rapidly or slowly. Can the children explain the changes?

Children's activity
20–25 mins
■ The children use the data on photocopiable page 48 to plot a graph, answer questions, then make and justify a prediction.

SCIENCE LINK ACTIVITY

The children compare the graph on photocopiable page 49 to a series of statements about a cyclist's progress in a cycle race, matching each statement to the appropriate part of the line graph.
(Answers: **1** A, **2** D, **3** F, **4** C, **5** E, **6** B.)

Differentiation
More able: Explain that the time when bulbs flower can vary by as much as 2 weeks, depending on the weather. Ask the children to suggest suitable dates for the visit.
Less able: You could give the children graph paper (or copies of resource page 126) with axes already drawn and labelled, or labels to put in the correct places. Give help with drawing the graph where necessary.

Plenary
10 mins
Discuss when is the best time to invite the visitor and why. What other things might give a curved line graph?

SCIENCE FOCUS: CHANGING STATE (QCA UNIT 5D)

Learning objectives
■ To obtain evidence by making careful observations.
■ To make predictions using scientific knowledge and understanding.
■ To know that melting is a change of state that can be reversed.

Resources
■ Small containers of crushed ice direct from a freezer (at below 0°C).
■ Thermometers, stopwatches or other timers, graph paper, rulers.
■ A copy of photocopiable pages 50 and 51 for each child.
Safety: Warn the children not to touch ice direct from the freezer: it can freeze to their fingers, causing painful 'frostbite'.

Introduction
5–10 mins
■ Ask the children to describe the states that water can be found in. (Liquid water, ice, water vapour/steam.) Discuss when water is found in each of these states, and establish that there is a link between the temperature and the state the water is in.
■ If necessary, explain the concept of water vapour. This is water in its gaseous state, and it is invisible. Mist and fog are not water vapour: they are suspensions of small water droplets in air. Steam is water vapour above 100°C; in air at a normal temperature and pressure, steam will quickly condense.

Whole-class, teacher-directed activity
15–20 mins
■ Show the children some ice and ask them to predict what will happen if it is left in the warm classroom. *How will the temperature change?* Record their predictions. Point out that the ice has been crushed, and discuss what effect this might have on the results. (Since more of the ice is in contact with the air, the ice will melt more quickly.)
■ Ask the children to find out how the temperature of the ice changes by taking measurements every 5 minutes until it has reached a temperature of 10°C. (The smaller the containers you use, the faster this will happen – but the fact that the temperature remains constant while the ice melts will be harder to observe.)
■ Ask the children to plot a graph to show their results. Give them a suitable range of values and units for each axis.

Children's activity
20–25 mins
■ Working in small groups, the children measure the temperature of melting ice at 5-minute intervals and plot a line graph. They can use photocopiable page 50 to record their results. Each group should discuss what the line graph shows, drawing a conclusion about what is happening while the temperature stays the same.
■ The children then use their graph to help them complete photocopiable page 51, labelling the stages of a heating curve for water.

Differentiation
More able: The children can complete all the questions on page 51, relating what they have found out about water to the melting and boiling of other substances.
Less able: The children may need help to complete the first part of page 51; they should not be expected to complete the second part.

Links to other topics
Technology/science: Melting and boiling different food ingredients. For example, chocolate can be melted over a pan of warm water – relate this to what happens to chocolate in hot weather.

GRAPHS TO SHOW CHANGES

Spring beauty

This table shows how the number of bulbs in flower at Hill Top Primary School changed over the first 12 weeks of the spring term.

Week	1	2	3	4	5	6
Number of flowers	0	0	10	40	70	120

Week	7	8	9	10	11	12
Number of flowers	140	140	140	120	100	80

■ Plot a graph to show how the number of bulbs in flower at Hill Top Primary School changes.

When was the number of bulbs in flower increasing most rapidly? _____

When was the number of bulbs in flower not changing? _____

When was the number of bulbs in flower decreasing? _____

When would you invite a gardening expert to visit the school? Why?

_____

_____

_____

NOW TRY THIS The time when bulbs flower can vary by 2 weeks, depending on the weather. How might this affect the time when you would invite the visitor?

The cycle race

This graph shows how the speed of a cyclist changed during a cycle race.

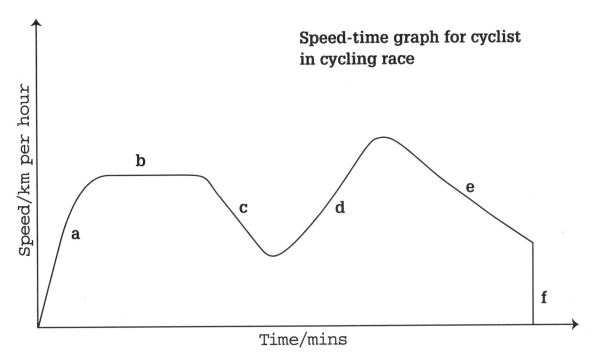

Speed-time graph for cyclist in cycling race

Each of the statements below describes what was happening at some point in the race.

◼ Match each statement to the correct letter on the graph.

1. The cyclist had plenty of energy and was speeding up quickly. _____

2. The cyclist was going downhill. _____

3. The cyclist had finished the race. _____

4. The cyclist was going uphill. _____

5. The cyclist was getting tired. _____

6. The cyclist was pedalling along the flat. _____

GRAPHS TO SHOW CHANGES

Observing how ice melts

◼ Draw a diagram to show how you measured the temperature of melting ice.

◼ Explain briefly what you did.

_____

_____

_____

◼ Use this table to record your results.

Time in minutes	Temperature in °C	Time in minutes	Temperature in °C

◼ Plot a graph to show how the temperature of the ice changed with time.

◼ Explain what was happening at each important point on your graph.

_____

_____

_____

_____

◼ On the back of this sheet, write a conclusion to describe how the temperature of ice changes when it melts.

Heating and cooling curves

■ Look at the heating curve for water and the labels in the box below it.
Write the letters for the labels in the correct places on the curve.

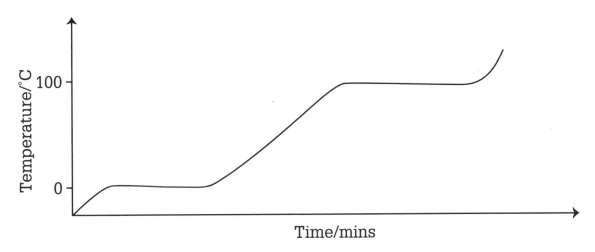

A: Ice warming   **B:** Melting point of ice

C: Boiling point of water   **D:** Water boiling   **E:** Steam heating

F: Ice melting   **G:** Water warming

■ Now look at these heating and cooling curves for other materials.
Use the facts below to help you decide which curve belongs to which substance.

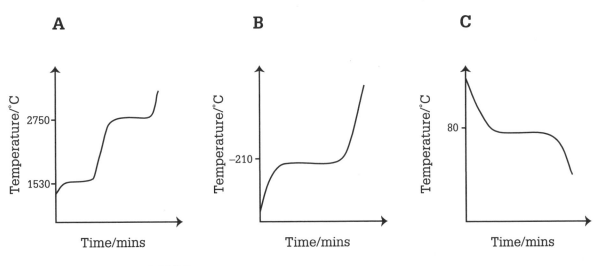

Nitrogen boils at –210°C. _____
Alcohol boils at 78°C. _____
Iron melts at 1535°C. _____

NOW
TRY
THIS

What state will alcohol be in at 90°C?
What state will nitrogen be in at room temperature?

WHAT DO YOU THINK?

MATHS FOCUS: DRAWING AND INTERPRETING BAR CHARTS

Learning objectives

- To test a hypothesis about the frequency of an event by collecting data.
- To discuss a bar chart showing the frequency of the event and check the original prediction.

Resources

- A board or flip chart, pens.
- A copy of photocopiable pages 54, 55 and 56, and resource pages 124 and 127 for each child; A3 copies of photocopiable page 55 and resource page 124.

Introduction

5 mins

- Make an imprecise statement, such as *Our school football team usually scores 3 or more goals*. Ask the children: *Do you think this statement is true? Could we test it?* Identify the points that make this statement hard to test. (What does 'usually' mean? What period of time are we talking about?) Help the children to reword the statement in a form that can be tested.

Whole-class, teacher-directed activity

20–25 mins

- Write the new statement (for example, *This school year our football team has scored 3 or more goals in over half their matches*) on the board. Ask the children what information must be collected to test the statement. *How should we record the information?*
- Collect and record the information. Now help the children to plot a bar chart on the A3 copy of resource page 124.
- Ask questions such as: *In how many matches did the team score 5 goals? In what proportion of their matches did they score no goals?* Encourage volunteers to explain how they can use the bar chart to answer these questions.
- Show the children the A3 copy of photocopiable page 55. Fill this in using a show of hands. For the second and third questions, children may raise their hands for more than one answer. Ask the children to suggest statements or predictions they could investigate using data from the questionnaire.

Children's activity

20–25 mins

- Using the information on the class questionnaire, the children work in pairs to draw a bar chart in order to test either one of the statements on photocopiable page 54, or a statement of their own. They should use their bar chart to identify the most and least common values, then identify and record three other pieces of information they can derive from the bar chart.

SCIENCE LINK ACTIVITY

The children use photocopiable page 56 to help them record the different types of sounds they can hear outside their classroom, then draw a bar chart to help them answer the questions on the sheet. Resource page 127 can be used to help with recording.

Differentiation

More able: Encourage the children to use the bar chart to make comparisons and statements about the proportions of different values (for example, *Over half of the pets owned by our class are cats* rather than *The most popular pet is a cat*).

Less able: Help the children, where necessary, to use their bar chart to decide whether or not the statement was correct.

Plenary

10 mins

Discuss who might want to record data to test a statement or prediction. (For example: shopkeepers deciding what types of goods to stock; doctors needing to know the age range of people in their area in order to predict what illnesses they will have to treat.)

SCIENCE FOCUS: CHANGING SOUNDS (QCA UNIT 5F)

Learning objective
■ To know that some materials are effective in preventing sound vibrations from reaching the ear.

Resources
■ A range of materials suitable for muffling sound (bubble wrap, foam padding, duvet stuffing, blanket material, artificial fur and so on).
■ A source of constant-volume sound (such as a ticking clock), metre rulers.
■ A copy for each child of photocopiable page 57 and resource page 124.

Introduction
5–10 mins
■ Discuss reasons why it is sometimes important to prevent sounds travelling. Discuss some of the ways in which this is done. Can the children identify any of the materials that are used? Can they make any generalisations about the materials that are good for preventing sounds from travelling?

Whole-class, teacher-directed activity
20–25 mins
■ Show the children a range of 'earmuff' materials. Ask for suggestions about how these could be tested. (Material can be wrapped around a sound source or used to cover the ear.) **Safety:** warn the children that it is dangerous to put objects or materials in the ear unless they have been specifically designed for this (for example, earplugs).
■ Discuss what factor must be varied and what factor must be measured to compare the different materials. The children will need either to keep the thickness of the test material constant and measure the distance at which the sound source becomes inaudible or keep the distance constant and measure the thickness of the test material needed to make the sound source inaudible.
■ Ask the children to consider, while they are doing their investigation, how reliable their comparisons are and whether there are any factors that might make the comparisons unfair. (For example, if they use one layer of material each time, are the layers of different materials the same thickness?) Their ideas can be discussed in a plenary session.

Children's activity
20–25 mins
■ The children work in small groups, using photocopiable page 57 to guide and record their investigation. They should first predict which material will make the best earmuffs, and justify their choice. They should then investigate the different materials, deciding for themselves what to vary and what to measure. They should plot a bar chart to show their results, and use this to decide whether or not their original prediction was correct.

Differentiation
More able: Ask the children to identify places in their home where materials prevent sound from travelling. For each example, they should decide whether this is what the material was meant to do, or whether it was there for some other purpose (such as keeping us warm).
Less able: Help the children, where necessary, to plan their investigation. Ask them to tell you what things they are keeping the same and why this is important.

Links to other topics
Music: Compose music with loud and quiet passages. Can they find more than one way to produce quiet sounds from instruments that are normally loud?
Literacy: Write a letter of complaint to the local authority (at the Council Offices) about some form of noise pollution. Compose a suitable reply from an environmental health officer.

WHAT DO YOU THINK?

Using our class questionnaire

Here are three predictions about our class:

■ More than half the families in our class have at least one car.
■ Over half the children in our class have either swimming lessons or football lessons.
■ Less than one quarter of the pets owned by children in our class are rabbits.

■ Using information from your class questionnaire, find out whether one of these predictions (or a prediction of your own) is correct.

The prediction we will investigate is:

_____

_____

■ Use the bar graph resource sheet to draw a bar graph of your data.

■ Write down three things that your bar graph tells you.

1. _____

_____

2. _____

_____

3. _____

_____

NOW TRY THIS Which bar on your bar graph shows the largest number of children? What proportion is this (approximately) of the children in your class?

Our class questionnaire

How many cars does your family own?

0 cars ☐   1 car ☐

2 cars ☐   > 2 cars ☐

What out-of-school activities do you do?

Swimming ☐   Football ☐

Dance ☐   Music ☐   Other ☐

What pets do you own?

Dog ☐   Cat ☐

Rabbit ☐   Other ☐   No pets ☐

How do you travel to school?

Car ☐   Bus ☐

Bike ☐   Walk ☐

WHAT DO YOU THINK?

What sounds can we hear?

■ Stand in silence outside your classroom for 2 minutes.
Use the tally chart sheet to record all the different sounds that you hear.
Record the total number of times you hear each sound.

■ Fill in this table to show the greatest number of times each sound was heard by someone in your class.

Sound	Most times heard

■ Use the bar graph sheet to draw a bar graph showing the data.

What sound was the least common? _____

What sound was the most common? _____

NOW TRY THIS What proportion of all the sounds heard did the most common sound make up?

WHAT DO YOU THINK?

The best material for earmuffs

▊ Predict which material will be the most suitable for making earmuffs.

_____

Why do you think this material will be the best?

_____

_____

▊ Describe briefly how you will test the different materials. Say what you will change and what you will measure.

_____

_____

_____

_____

▊ Use the space below to record your results.

```



```

▊ Draw a bar chart to compare the effect of the different materials.

Was your original prediction correct? _____

NOW TRY THIS Describe some places in your home where materials prevent sound from travelling. Is that the main reason the material is there?

HANDLING AND INTERPRETING DATA

WHAT TIME?

MATHS FOCUS: INTERPRETING AND DRAWING LINE GRAPHS

Learning objectives
- To draw and interpret a line graph.

Resources
- A board or flip chart, pens.
- Graph paper or copies of resource page 126 (A4 for children, an A3 sheet for display), rulers, coloured pencils.
- A copy of photocopiable pages 60 (page 61 for less able children) and 62 for each child.

Introduction
10 mins
- Ask: *What is a bar graph?* Ask a volunteer to draw one on the board. *What is a line graph?* Ask a volunteer to draw one. Point out that a bar graph can have any set of values along the x-axis, but on a line graph the values have to change steadily (be continuous).

Whole-class, teacher-directed activity
20 mins
- Explain that line graphs often show how something changes as time goes by. Label the x-axis of a line graph 'Minutes' and ask the children to suggest something that could be recorded over several minutes (pulse rate after running, temperature of a cup of tea cooling down). *What could we record on a line graph with hours* (how far the tide comes up the beach), *days* (how much rain has fallen), *years* (how tall a child has grown)?
- Use the A3 graph paper and the information in the table below to help the children plot a graph to show how the time an athlete takes to run 100m changes over several weeks of training. Discuss what label to write on each axis, what scales to use and where to plot the points. Join up all the points with a jagged line (most of the children will not yet be ready for the idea of a 'best fit' line).

Weeks	1	2	3	4	5	6	7	8	9	10
Time to run 100m (s)	20	19	18	17	18	19	18	17	16	15

- Discuss what the graph means. Make sure the children understand that a faster athlete will have a shorter time. *When was the athlete getting faster/slower? When might she have been on holiday and done less training for 2 weeks?*

Children's activity
20–25 mins
- The children use page 60 to plot a graph showing how the distance run by another athlete in 5 minutes changes over several weeks of training. They then answer some questions by interpreting the graph.

Differentiation
More able: Ask the children to draw a second line on the graph showing how the distance would change if the athlete improved steadily. *How many weeks would it take for him to run 900m in 5 minutes?*
Less able: The children could complete page 61, plotting their graph on the labelled axes provided.

Plenary
10 mins
Look at the graphs the children have drawn. Discuss whether the intermediate values on the graph have any meaning (yes – for example, after about 10 days the athlete would have been able to run about 625m in 5 minutes).

SCIENCE LINK ACTIVITY

Photocopiable page 62 provides data about the relative amount of solar energy collected by a solar energy panel at different times of the year. The children should use the data to plot a line graph, then relate the graph to their knowledge about the relative amounts of sunlight in different seasons.

SCIENCE FOCUS: EARTH, SUN AND MOON (QCA UNIT 5E)

Learning objectives
- To present times of sunrise and sunset as a line graph.
- To interpret a graph, identifying trends and patterns in the results.

Resources
- Diaries or newspapers with sunrise and sunset times, rulers, coloured pencils.
- A copy of photocopiable page 63 and a sheet of A4 graph paper for each child.

Introduction
10 mins
- Recap the children's knowledge of the apparent movement of the Sun. Emphasise that it is the Earth that moves, not the Sun. Ask the children to describe some of the effects of the Sun's apparent motion (changes in the length and direction of shadows; day and night; the seasons). Help them to explain these in terms of the Earth's rotation and orbit.

Whole-class, teacher-directed activity
20 mins
- Discuss the children's experience of sunrise and sunset in different seasons: getting up in the dark in winter, long summer evenings and so on. Show them how to find sunrise and sunset times in published diaries or newspapers. Emphasise that these times change steadily throughout the year. Discuss how a 'middle' time for each month is worked out. (Choose the time given for the date closest to the 15th, and round to the nearest half-hour.) The figures on photocopiable page 63 have been adjusted to ignore daylight saving time.
- Discuss how sunrise and sunset times could be recorded on a line graph. *What should we put on the x-axis?* (Time usually, so the months of the year in this case.) *What scales should we use for each axis?* (On 1cm graph paper, set as portrait, the graph fits well with 1cm = 1 month for the x-axis and 1cm = 1 hour for the y-axis.) *Should we use approximate sunrise and sunset times?* (Yes, round them to the nearest half-hour.)
- Discuss the advantage of plotting the lines for sunrise and sunset on the same axes: they can be compared to show how the amount of daylight changes throughout the year.

Children's activity
20–25 mins
- Working in pairs, the children should use the sunrise and sunset times given on page 63 to plot one graph with separate lines for sunrise and sunset. Suitable scales are suggested above; the values on the y-axis could go either from 0–22 hours or from 2–22 hours. At this stage, most children will probably feel more confident with a scale beginning at 0.
- The children should then answer the questions, relating the graph to their knowledge of changing day-length in different seasons.

Differentiation
More able: Ask the children to work in a group to predict how the lines would change if they took account of daylight saving time. (They do not need to draw the new lines.) Can they explain the effect that daylight saving time would have on the total amount of daylight in the summer? (No effect at all.)
Less able: Help the children to decide on labels for the axes and the range of numbers on the y-axis of their graph. Help them to work out which part of their graph represents the daylight time.

Links to other topics
Geography: Different patterns of seasons in different climates. **Art:** Making seasonal collages or paintings, choosing materials and colours appropriate to the season they have chosen.

WHAT TIME?

Training for the Big Fun Run

Gregory is training to run in his town's Big Fun Run. He asked his friends to record how far he could run in 5 minutes.
Here are the results they collected.

Week	Distance in metres
1	600
2	650
3	700
4	Didn't measure
5	650
6	700
7	800
8	850
9	900
10	900

■ Plot a graph to show how the distance that Gregory ran in 5 minutes changed with the number of weeks he had been training. Remember to give your graph a title and label the axes.

When did Gregory run 700m in 5 minutes? _____

When did Gregory's speed increase the most? _____

When do you think Gregory went on holiday for 2 weeks?

_____

NOW TRY THIS Gregory improved steadily until Week 3. If he had kept up this rate of improvement, when would he have run 900m in 5 minutes?

The Fun Run

Gregory is training for a Fun Run.
This table shows how far he can run in 5 minutes.

Week	Distance in metres
1	500
2	600
3	700
4	800
5	850
6	900

Plot a graph of the distance Gregory can run in 5 minutes against the number of weeks he has been training.

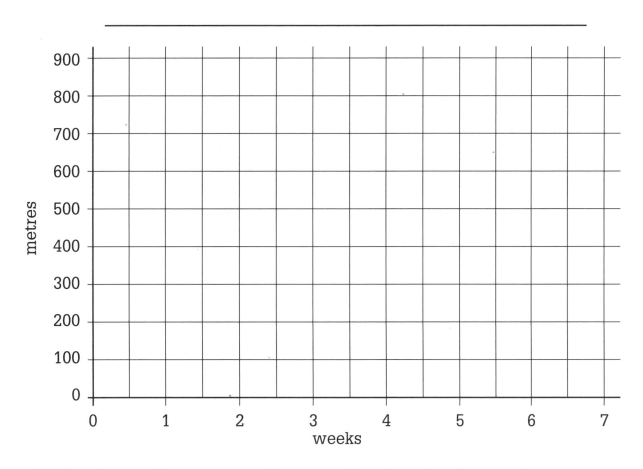

1. How far can Gregory run in 5 minutes after 4 weeks of training? _____

2. Is he getting faster or slower with training? How do you know?

_____

WHAT TIME?

Solar-powered safety lights

A marker buoy at sea has a solar panel to collect sunlight in order to charge the battery for its flashing safety light.

A meter measures the number of units of sunlight that are collected. 10 is strong sunlight, 0 is no sunlight.

Here are the results:

Month	January	February	March	April
Meter reading	5	6	7	8
Month	May	June	July	August
Meter reading	9	10	10	9
Month	September	October	November	December
Meter reading	8	6	5	4

▨ Plot a graph to show the meter readings through the year. Remember to:
  ▪ give your graph a title
  ▪ label your axes.

▨ Draw a line to join up the points on your graph.

1. When was the most sunlight collected to charge the battery? _____

2. When was the least sunlight collected to charge the battery? _____

3. How many units of sunlight were collected in April? _____

4. Why do you think the amount of sunlight collected varied throughout the year?

_____

_____

NOW TRY THIS How do you think the weather might affect the amount of sunlight collected?

WHAT TIME?

Sunrise and sunset

Sunrise and sunset times change through the year.
This table shows how they change in London.

Month	Sunrise time
January	8:00
February	7:00
March	6:00
April	5:00
May	4:00
June	3:30
July	4:00
August	5:00
September	6:00
October	7:00
November	8:00
December	8.30

Month	Sunset time
January	16:30
February	17:30
March	18:00
April	19:00
May	19:30
June	20:30
July	19:30
August	19:00
September	18:00
October	17:30
November	16:30
December	16:00

■ Plot a graph of sunrise time against month. Use a coloured pencil.

■ Plot a graph of sunset time against month on the same axes. Use a different-coloured pencil.

1. When does the Sun rise earliest? _____

2. When does the Sun set earliest? _____

■ Use a coloured pencil to shade very lightly the area of your graph that shows when it is daylight.

When are there most hours of daylight? _____

NOW TRY THIS Discuss how the graph would be different if it showed daylight saving time. How would this affect the number of hours of daylight?

THE TRUTH IS OUT THERE

ENQUIRY AND INVESTIGATION

MATHS FOCUS: COLLECTING, ORGANISING AND INTERPRETING DATA

Learning objective
■ To solve a problem by collecting, organising and interpreting data.

Resources
■ Graph paper, a copy of photocopiable pages 66 and 67 for each child, access to resource pages 124–127.
Note: You will need to record a video of about 20 advertisements for a range of products.

Introduction
5–10 mins
■ Tell the children they are going to carry out a complete investigation to try to answer a question. Suggest two questions they could investigate: *What types of television programme do the children in our class watch?* and *What types of television advertisements are effective?* Encourage them to suggest more questions to investigate.

Whole-class, teacher-directed activity
20–25 mins
■ Decide as a class what question to investigate. It should be one that allows the children to collect more than one type of data, and to record and present the data in more than one form.
■ Discuss some further questions the children may need to ask in order to determine what data to collect and what comparisons to make. For example, to investigate the question *What types of teevision programme do the children in our class watch?* the children need to ask: *What categories shall we divide programmes into? How shall we decide which category a particular programme is in? Shall we ask only about programmes the children watched last night, or ones they watched last week, or all the programmes they have ever watched?*
■ Explain that each group will have to decide what information they are going to collect. They will also have to decide the best way to record their information. Remind them of some familiar ways of recording information, such as tally charts and tables, and discuss the types of information that might be recorded in these ways.
■ The groups will also have to decide on the best way to present the information they collect, so that it is as easy as possible to interpret. Discuss some ways of presenting results: bar charts, line graphs and pie charts. Ask the children when they might use each of these methods. The 'best' way for each group will depend on what they want to find out.

Children's activity
25–30 mins
■ The children work in groups to investigate one of the questions from the introduction, or a question of their own. All of the children should investigate the same question to allow comparison of different methods and results. If you choose to investigate television advertising, all the children should watch the video of advertisements before beginning their investigation. Photocopiable pages 66 and 67, and resource pages 124–127 may be used to help with planning, recording and presenting the results. Encourage the groups to draw a conclusion, and to assess its validity and possible limitations.

Differentiation
More able: Encourage the children to suggest ways to improve their investigation.
Less able: Help the children decide what data to collect. Suggest a way of recording and presenting their results.

SCIENCE LINK ACTIVITY

The data-handling skills developed in this lesson can be applied to science investigations on a range of themes in other lessons.

Plenary
10 mins
Ask each group to tell the class what results they collected and what conclusions they drew. Ask them to describe any problems or limitations of their investigation – for example, 'We only asked 20 children. That was probably not enough to draw a conclusion' or 'We didn't ask about wildlife programmes.'

SCIENCE FOCUS: ENQUIRY IN ENVIRONMENTAL AND TECHNOLOGICAL CONTEXTS (QCA UNIT 5/6H)

Learning objectives

- To plan a suitable approach to an investigation.
- To collect and record evidence in an appropriate manner.
- To use scientific knowledge and understanding to explain results.
- To evaluate evidence and results and consider their limitations.

Resources

- Metre rulers, tape measures or 30cm rulers, access to a low-powered microscope.
- Clear plastic drinks bottles, measuring beakers or cylinders.
- A variety of filtering materials (such as sand, filter paper, cotton wool, fabric).
- A copy of photocopiable pages 68 and 69 for each child.

Note: The length of time the children need to spend on their investigation will vary enormously. Building in flexibility will allow all the children to gain the maximum value from this activity.

Introduction

10 mins

- Tell the children that they are going to carry out a complete investigation. Recap on the stages of an investigation: decide on a question to investigate, express the question in a form that can be tested, decide what information to collect and how to record it, present the results in a form that is easy to interpret, draw a conclusion, assess any limitations and consider possible improvements.

Whole-class, teacher-directed activity

20 mins

- As a class, decide on a question to investigate, such as *How do dandelions in long grass and short grass differ?* or *What is an effective way to clean dirty water?* (These are supported by photocopiable pages 68 and 69.) Other possible problems to investigate might be: *Do different small animals live in water from different depths of a pond? Are the first plants to grow in bare soil always the same type? Can we design a burglar alarm for the class cupboard? How could we use elastic bands to make a weighing machine?* Other questions might be suggested by the children's interest in an aspect of one of their science topics.
- Help the children to suggest possible ways of expressing the question so that it can be tested. Discuss the information that would have to be collected in each case. Ask each group to decide what information they will collect and how they will record it.
- Discuss how we can decide whether or not an investigation has given a valid result. *What questions should we ask ourselves?* Encourage the children to ask questions such as: *Was our sample size big enough? Could the results we saw have been caused by something we didn't measure? Could we have made our measurements or observations more accurate?*

Children's activity

25–30 mins or longer

- The children work in groups to investigate the class question. Each group decides what data to collect and how to record and present it. They can use photocopiable pages 68 and 69 for guidance. They should discuss the accuracy of their results and the limitations of their investigation, deciding whether or not they can draw a valid conclusion from these results.

Differentiation

More able: Encourage the children to suggest ways of improving their investigation.
Less able: The children may need help with planning what to do. Help them to discuss their results, and to explain them using scientific language.

Links to other topics

Design and technology: Many possible investigations might require the children to build models, using design and technology skills.
Literacy: Writing explanations of how different machines work and were designed and made.

THE TRUTH IS OUT THERE

What do we watch on TV?

■ Write down a question that you can test.

_____

_____

What categories (groups) will you divide television programmes into?

_____

_____

_____

■ Write down the question or questions you will ask to find out what the children in your class watch.

_____

_____

_____

■ Record and present your results in the best way you can find.

■ Explain why the way you have chosen is the best.

_____

_____

What have you found out from your investigation?

_____

_____

_____

■ Discuss any problems or limitations of your investigation. Describe them.

_____

_____

_____

NOW TRY THIS Describe any ways in which your investigation could be improved.

THE TRUTH IS OUT THERE

How effective is TV advertising?

Your teacher will show you some television advertisements.

▪ Watch them carefully, but do not write anything down.

▪ Make up a questionnaire that you could use to find out which advertisements were the most effective. Here is an example of a question for you to answer:

What brand names can you remember?

_____

_____

_____

▪ Now write your questionnaire on another sheet of paper. Use it to find the data you want. Remember to record and present your data clearly.

What do your results show?

_____

_____

_____

_____

▪ Discuss these questions:
  ▪ Did you collect enough information to reach a valid conclusion?
  ▪ Do you think your conclusion might have been different if you had asked a different group of people?
  ▪ How could you make your results more reliable or more accurate?
  ▪ Did your investigation have any limitations that affected the validity of the conclusions?

NOW TRY THIS Describe any ways in which your investigation could be improved.

THE TRUTH IS OUT THERE

Dandelions in long and short grass

■ Suggest how the dandelion plants in long grass might be different from those in short grass.

_____

_____

■ Write a question about the dandelions growing in long and short grass in a form that can be tested.

_____

_____

■ Describe what you will do to test this. Write where you will look at dandelion plants, what you will measure and how many plants you will study. Include a diagram if you wish.

```



```

■ Write a conclusion to say what you have found out.

_____

_____

Do you think your investigation gave a valid result? _____
■ Explain why.

_____

_____

_____

NOW TRY THIS Suggest any ways in which you could improve your investigation.

THE TRUTH IS OUT THERE

How can we clean dirty water?

Draw a labelled diagram of the equipment you will use to clean dirty water.

Class 5 made these suggestions about how they could tell how clean a sample of water was:

"We could drink it and decide what it tastes like."
"We could look at it under a microscope and see how many bits there are in it."
"We could put it in a beaker and measure what depth of water we could see through."
"We could look at it and see how clean it looked."

▨ Describe how you will find out how clean your water is. (Make sure you choose a **safe** way.)

_____

_____

_____

▨ If you have time, try modifying your equipment and using it to clean some more water. Does it do the job better this time?

▨ Compare your result with the results of other groups in your class.

▨ Describe the features of the best equipment that made it work so well.

_____

_____

_____

NOW TRY THIS Suggest any ways in which you could improve your investigation.

SOLVING PROBLEMS

FINDING THE ANSWERS

MATHS FOCUS: CHOOSING NUMBER OPERATIONS TO SOLVE PROBLEMS

Learning objectives
■ To choose and use appropriate number operations to solve problems given in word form.
■ To explain methods and reasoning, orally and in writing.

Resources
■ A board or flip chart, pens.
■ A copy of photocopiable pages 72 (page 73 for less able children) and 74 for each child.

Introduction
5 mins
■ Tell the children: *We all use maths every day to solve problems. Who can think of a time when we might use addition?* (Shopping is an obvious example.) Ask them to think of when they might use the other number operations. *Often the biggest problem is deciding what maths to use.*

Whole-class, teacher-directed activity
20 mins
■ Write this problem on the board: *Jo, Jim and Jack are going to share out a load of 30kg. Jim can carry 4kg more than Jo and Jack can carry 5kg more than Jo. How much should they each carry?*
■ Draw a stick figure carrying a bag on the board. *Here is Jo. How much is he carrying? We don't know, so we'll leave it blank.* Draw another stick figure carrying two bags. *Here is Jim. He is carrying the same amount as Jo, plus a bit extra. Do we know how much the extra bit is?* Label the extra bag '4kg'. Draw another figure to represent Jack, carrying an extra 5kg.
■ *Do we know how much Jo, Jim and Jack are carrying altogether?* (30kg.) Draw all of the bags together and write '= 30kg'. *How much would the load be if we took off Jim's extra bit?* (26kg.) *How much would it be if we took away Jack's extra bit as well?* (21kg.) *So the 3 loads left are the same, and make a total of 21kg. How much is each one?* (7kg.)
■ Refer to your stick figure pictures to work out how much Jo, Jim and Jack each carry. (7kg, 11kg and 12kg respectively.)

Children's activity
20–25 mins
■ The children work together in pairs or threes to solve the word problems on photocopiable page 72. Encourage them to draw pictures to describe the problem, and to explain to each other what they need to do.
■ Talk through the answers. For question 2, 36 scoops is 6 'sets' of green paint = 6 scoops of blue, 12 yellow and 18 white. For question 3 each day the snail moves 6m up the tree (8m less 2m that it slides down), so it takes 7 days to reach the top.

SCIENCE LINK ACTIVITY

Give the children copies of photocopiable page 74 to work through individually. Discuss their solutions. To calculate the amount of fudge made, it is necessary to consider the mass lost in the cooking process. The children should realise that this process is irreversible, since a new material has been made: the fudge cannot be 'unmixed'.

Differentiation
More able: Can the children 'work backwards' to produce similar problems to the ones on page 72 (using different numbers)?
Less able: The children can work together to solve the single-stage problems on photocopiable page 73.

Plenary
10 mins
Ask volunteers to suggest single- or multi-stage problems for the class to solve. Ask other children to volunteer solutions. Give help where necessary.

SOLVING PROBLEMS

SCIENCE FOCUS: REVERSIBLE AND IRREVERSIBLE CHANGES (QCA UNIT 6D)

Learning objectives
- To know that mixing materials can cause them to change.
- To know that some changes cannot easily be reversed.
- To make careful observations and explain these using scientific knowledge and understanding.

Resources
- A beaker of water, soluble paracetamol tablets, non-soluble paracetamol tablets.
- Accurate scientific scales (measuring to the nearest 1g).
- A copy of photocopiable page 75 for each child.

Safety: This is a teacher demonstration activity, since children should not handle medicines.

Introduction
5 mins
- Show the children the beaker of water. *Imagine I have a powder and you don't know what it is. If I drop it in here, tell me the three things it might do.* (Dissolve, like salt or sugar; do nothing, like sand or flour; change, like plaster of Paris or Andrew's Salts.)

Whole-class, teacher-directed activity
20 mins
- Show the children the paracetamol tablets. Remind them of the dangers of medication and why they must not touch these tablets.
- Hold up the soluble tablets. Ask: *What do you think these will do if we drop them in water?* Drop one into the beaker. Ask the children to describe what they can see happening. Now try a non-soluble tablet. *Which tablets might be easier to take? Why?* Discuss whether the soluble tablet can be recovered after dissolving, whether this is a reversible or an irreversible change, and why the mixture bubbles (one of the new materials made is a gas).
- Ask: *Can we find out how much gas is given off?* Discuss the children's suggestions. Remind them that no material 'disappears'. Prompt them to show what happens in picture form, as below.

- Use the scales to separately weigh a beaker of fresh water and two soluble paracetamol tablets. Give the children copies of page 75 for recording. Drop the tablets into the water and record the mass of the mixture after all the bubbling has stopped.

Children's activity
20–25 mins
- The children should use page 75 to record the teacher demonstration and describe what is happening in the form of a picture equation. They should then use the results to work out how much gas was given off when the tablets dissolved. (For two paracetamol tablets, it will be approximately 4g.)

Differentiation
More able: Ask the children to discuss the advantages of soluble painkillers over non-soluble ones. Can they suggest why the soluble tablets are much bigger than the non-soluble ones for the same amount of medicine?

Less able: Help the children, where necessary, to make and understand a picture equation for the reaction. Help them to put in the values they have recorded, and show them how to calculate the mass of gas given off.

Links to other topics
PSHE: The uses of medicines and the dangers of drug misuse. **Design and technology:** Designing a package for paracetamol tablets, with appropriate colouring and pictures to make it unattractive to young children.

SOLVING PROBLEMS **PHOTOCOPIABLE**

FINDING THE ANSWERS

Solving word problems

1. Kim is mixing green paint for a wall painting. The mixture she uses is:
- 1 scoop blue paint
- 2 scoops yellow paint
- 3 scoops white paint.

   Kim uses 8 scoops of blue paint. Write out and solve calculations to show how much yellow and white paint she will need.

_____

_____

2. Kim uses 36 scoops of paint altogether. How many scoops of each colour does she use?
(**Remember:** Drawing the problem in pictures makes it easier to answer.)

3. Each night, a snail climbs 8m up the trunk of a 40m high tree in the school grounds. Each day, it slides 2m down the trunk again. How many days will it be before the snail reaches the top of the tree?
(**Remember:** Draw pictures to help you show what is happening.)

NOW TRY THIS Make up some problems of your own like the ones you have just solved.

FINDING THE ANSWERS

Solving word problems

Kim is mixing green paint for a
wall painting. The mixture she uses is:

- 1 scoop blue paint
- 2 scoops yellow paint
- 3 scoops white paint.

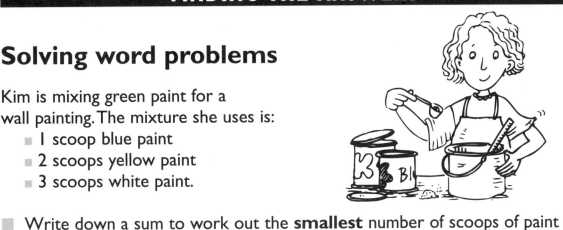

■ Write down a sum to work out the **smallest** number of scoops of paint
Kim can use altogether.

_____

■ Write down a sum to work out the **second smallest** number of scoops of
paint Kim can use.

_____

_____

If Kim used 5 scoops of blue paint:

How many scoops of yellow paint would she use?

_____

How many scoops of white paint would she use?

_____

How many scoops of paint would she use altogether?

_____

_____

 NOW TRY THIS If Kim used 12 scoops of yellow paint, how many scoops of
blue paint would she need?

■SCHOLASTIC **73**

FINDING THE ANSWERS

Making fudge

The recipe that Candy's Sweet Shop uses
to make fudge has the following ingredients:

- 50g butter
- 450g sugar
- 300g (300ml) milk.

When the fudge is cooked it loses $\frac{1}{10}$ (10%) of its mass.

If Candy's Sweet Shop used the quantities given in the recipe, what mass of
fudge would it make?

_____

If Candy's Sweet Shop used 150g of butter, what mass of fudge would it make?
(**Remember:** Drawing the problem in picture form makes it easier to solve.)

Could you 'unmix' the fudge to get the ingredients back again? _____

■ Explain your answer.

_____

_____

_____

NOW TRY THIS   How much fudge would you make if you started with 1350g
of sugar?

Dissolving paracetamol tablets

■ Draw or describe briefly what your teacher did.

Was the change you saw reversible or irreversible? _____
■ Explain why.

_____

_____

■ Use this table to record your measurements.

What we measured	Value

■ Draw a picture equation to show what happened.

■ Work out how much gas was given off when the paracetamol tablets dissolved.

_____

_____

NOW TRY THIS Suggest one advantage of using soluble paracetamol tablets instead of insoluble ones.

WHAT PROPORTION?

MATHS FOCUS: MEASURING AND CALCULATING AREAS

Learning objective
- To measure the area of an irregular shape.

Resources
- A board or flip chart marked with a square grid, pens.
- Squared paper or graph paper, coloured pencils, tracing paper, paper clips.
- A copy of photocopiable pages 78 (page 79 for less able children) and 80, and resource page 126 for each child.
- A range of irregular shapes and irregular-shaped objects to draw round.

Introduction
5–10 mins
- Show children two 2-D shapes of clearly different sizes. Ask: *Which shape has the larger area?* Show two 2-D shapes of similar area. *Which of these two has the larger area? How could we find out?* Discuss the children's ideas. Emphasise the need for careful measurement. When the areas are clearly very close, estimating may give the wrong answer.

Whole-class, teacher-directed activity
10–15 mins
- Draw round two similar-sized shapes on squared paper or a square grid. Help the children calculate the area of each shape.
- Count and record the number of whole squares. *Is this bigger or smaller than the real area? Why?* Help the children to decide what else must be counted. Either count areas more than ½ square and ignore the smaller areas, or add together various 'bits' of squares to make whole squares. Ask the children which method they think is better.
- Discuss the effect on overall accuracy of changing the size of the squares used. (Smaller squares will give a more accurate answer.)
- Help the children to calculate the area of the whole page (by multiplying length by width) and then to find the approximate proportion of the page that the shape covers, either as a fraction or as a percentage (for example, *more than 10% and less than 25%*).

Children's activity
20–25 mins
- The children find the area of the shape on photocopiable page 78. They then choose a shape of their own and follow both sets of instructions on page 78 to find its area, comparing the accuracy of the answers found using large and small squares and suggesting a reason why the small squares give a more accurate answer.

SCIENCE LINK ACTIVITY

Give each child a copy of photocopiable page 80. This tells them how to find the proportion of a picture that is black (for example) by tracing the picture, marking the parts that are black, then placing the tracing paper over a square grid. The children can practise this with a picture of their own.

Differentiation
More able: Ask the children to draw as many of their shape as possible on the grid of large squares on page 126. What proportion of the grid have they covered? Ask them what shapes they think would be best and worst at filling all the space.

Less able: Let the children use photocopiable page 79. Do they think their answer would be bigger or smaller if they used paper with smaller squares?

Plenary
10 mins
Ask the children to explain how they found out what proportion of the page their shape took up. Keep to simple fractions or percentages, such as 'less than ¼' or 'a bit more than 10%'.

SCIENCE FOCUS: MICRO-ORGANISMS (QCA UNIT 6B)

Learning objectives
- To know that micro-organisms can cause food to decay.
- To know that food must be handled and stored with care.

Resources
- Samples of mouldy food (such as fruit or vegetables).
- Slices of bread (mould shows more clearly on wholemeal bread, and bread with the minimum of preservatives will go mouldy faster).
- Clear, sealable plastic bags.
- Squared or graph paper, tracing paper.
- A copy of photocopiable page 81 for each child.

Safety: All mouldy food must be kept in see-through, sealed containers as children may be allergic to the mould spores.

Introduction
5 mins
- Show the children the samples of mouldy food. Ask: *What has happened to these?* Discuss their ideas about when food goes mouldy and what causes it. Explain that micro-organisms are making the food decay. We can see the mould, but some micro-organisms that cause decay are too small to see.

Whole-class, teacher-directed activity
10 mins
- Ask: *When will food go mouldy most quickly? How could we find out?* Discuss how the bread could be used to test the best conditions for mould growth. Help the children to decide on suitable conditions to place the bread in (such as damp/dry or hot/warm/cold) and what changes to look for. Small patches of mould can be hard to spot, so it is easier to compare the amount of mould on different slices of bread after about two weeks.
- Discuss why the bread must be kept in sealed bags (danger from mould spores) and how the mould gets in if the bag is sealed (there are mould spores in the air around us all the time, so some will be sealed in the bag with the bread).
- Recap on how to use the 'drawing and counting' of squares method to find the area of each slice of bread that is mouldy. A square grid drawn on tracing paper and placed over the bread will make the area easier to copy onto squared paper.

Children's activity
20–25 mins
- Working in small groups, the children use photocopiable page 81 to help them measure and record how much of a slice of bread is covered by mould. Each group should compare the area of mould on two or more slices of bread kept in different conditions, then decide which conditions are best for growing mould. In a plenary session, ask the children to explain what they have found out. Use this as a starting point for discussing ideas about the best storage conditions for food.

Differentiation
More able: The children should work out the proportion of each slice of bread that is mouldy.
Less able: The children may need help in working out the areas. They could count only those squares that are completely covered by mould.

Links to other topics
Literacy: Make illustrated leaflets or posters presenting simple food hygiene rules.
Literacy/Drama: Write and perform mini-plays to illustrate the dangers of keeping food in unhygienic conditions.

WHAT PROPORTION?

Finding areas

■ Find the area of this shape.

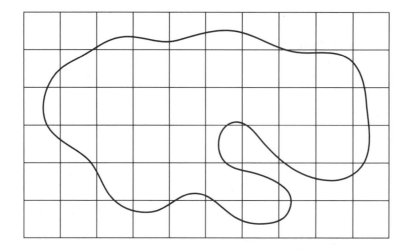

■ Write a sentence to explain how you counted the bits that were not whole squares.

_____

_____

■ Choose an irregular shape. Follow these instructions to find its area.
1. Draw round your shape in the top left corner a grid of large squares.
2. Count the squares to find the area.

■ Now follow these instructions for a different method.
1. Draw round your shape on the grid of small squares on the grid of small squares.
2. Count the squares to find the area.
3. Calculate the number of large squares this is equal to (1 large square = 4 small squares).

Which method gives a more accurate value for
the shape's area: the first method or the second? _____

■ Write a sentence to explain why.

_____

_____

**NOW
TRY
THIS**
Draw your shape as many times as you can on the grid of large squares. What proportion of the grid have you covered?

Finding areas

■ Follow the instructions to find the area of this shape.

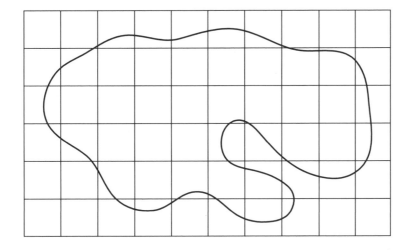

1. Count the number of whole squares.

Write your answer here. _____

2. Count all the bits that are more than half a square.

Write your answer here. _____

3. Add your two answers together to find the area. _____

4. Complete this sentence.

The area of the shape is _____ squares.

NOW TRY THIS

If you drew round this shape on paper with smaller squares, would your answer be bigger or smaller?

WHAT PROPORTION?

What proportion is it?

What proportion of this horse is black?
■ Follow the instructions to find out.

1. Trace the picture. Shade in the parts that are black.
2. Fasten your tracing over graph paper or squared paper.
3. Count the squares to find the area of the whole horse.

Record it here. _____

■ Fill in this table.

Fraction of horse	Number of squares (to nearest whole number)	Percentage of horse
1		100%
$\frac{3}{4}$		75%
$\frac{1}{2}$		50%
$\frac{1}{4}$		25%

■ Now count squares to find the area of the black patches.

Record it here. _____

■ Write a sentence to say what proportion of the horse is black, either as a fraction or as a percentage.

_____

_____

NOW TRY THIS   Repeat this with a two-colour picture of your own.

WHAT PROPORTION?

How much bread is mouldy?

■ Look at the slices of bread you have kept in different conditions. For each slice, find out how much is mouldy.

1. Make a life-sized drawing of the bread on squared paper.

2. Label your drawing with the conditions the bread was kept in.

3. Count the squares to find the area of the whole slice.

4. Shade the areas that are mouldy.

5. Count the shaded squares to find the total area of the mouldy bits. Record the mouldy area on the drawing.

■ Repeat this for each of your slices of bread.

■ Write a sentence to describe the conditions that made the most mould grow on the bread.

_____

_____

NOW TRY THIS   Work out what proportion of each slice of bread is mouldy.

HOW CAN WE MEASURE IT?

MATHS FOCUS: SUGGESTING SUITABLE UNITS FOR MEASURING

Learning objective
■ To suggest and use suitable measuring instruments and units.

Resources
■ A board or flip chart, pens.
■ A beaker, a dropper, a child's toy windmill, a pad of Post-It Notes.
■ Tracing paper, coloured felt-tipped pens, 30cm rulers, measuring scales, a 5ml measuring spoon, paper clips, blank paper.
■ A copy of photocopiable pages 84 (page 85 for less able children) and 86 for each child.

Introduction
10 mins
■ Check the children's knowledge of the standard units for length, mass and capacity: *What units would you use to measure the width of the playground... the mass of a cat?* and so on. Ask them to suggest things they could not measure using the units they are familiar with, such as the thickness of a sheet of paper or the mass of a grass seed. List their suggestions.

Whole-class, teacher-directed activity
20–25 mins
■ Hold up a pad of Post-It Notes. Tear one off and ask: *How much does this Post-It Note weigh? How could I find out?* If necessary, prompt the children to consider the mass of the whole pad and the number of notes it contains. Weigh the pad of notes and use this to calculate the mass of one note.
■ Show the children one drip of water from a dropper and ask: *How could we find the volume of just one drop of water?* Find out how many drops fill a 5ml measuring spoon and use this to calculate the volume of one drop.
■ Discuss how standard units could be used to find other 'unusual' things. Use the children's windmill to 'measure' wind strength. Demonstrate that a strong blow makes the windmill spin fast and a gentle blow hardly makes it move at all. Measure different wind strengths by counting the number of turns in 5 minutes.
■ Other possible things to measure are loudness of sound (what thickness of material it can be heard through) and runniness of liquid (how far one drop rolls down a slope in a given time).

Children's activity
20–25 mins
■ The children work together to find the mass of a paper clip and the thickness of a sheet of paper, using photocopiable page 84 for recording. They then plan ways to compare the smoothness of different slopes, again recording their ideas on page 84. (They could measure how far an object slides down the slope in a given time, or how long it takes to slide a given distance.)

SCIENCE LINK ACTIVITY
Photocopiable page 86 can be used to plan and carry out a comparison of how well different-coloured felt-tipped pens 'show up'. The children can do this either by measuring the distance from which a written message can be read or by comparing the number of sheets of tracing paper through which it can be read. They should recognise that the size of the letters and the lighting conditions also affect how well the message can be seen.

Differentiation
More able: Can the children think of other 'unusual' things they could measure using standard units? They could work in pairs to discuss ways of measuring these variables.
Less able: The children can use photocopiable page 85, which provides step-by-step instructions for finding the mass of a paper clip.

Plenary
10 mins
Remind the children of the main variables they can measure using standard units: mass, length, capacity and time. Recap on how these can be used to measure some 'unusual' things.

SCIENCE FOCUS: CHANGING CIRCUITS (QCA UNIT 6G)

Learning objective

- To know that the brightness of bulbs in a circuit can be changed.

Resources

- Batteries, bulbs, wires, tracing paper, metre rulers.
- A copy of photocopiable page 87 for each child.

Introduction

5 mins

- Discuss the children's experience of the brightness of bulbs. *Where have you seen very bright or very dim bulbs?* Have they used a 'dimmer switch'? Can they describe what happens to the brightness of a torch bulb when the battery is 'going flat' and needs changing?

Whole-class, teacher-directed activity

10 mins

- Ask the children to suggest how they could compare the brightness of different bulbs, since they do not have a meter that measures 'brightness'. If necessary, prompt them to think about distant lights and lights shining through materials.
- There are two ways to compare the brightness of bulbs: to see how far away the bulb can be seen from or to find out what it will shine through (for example, how many sheets of tracing paper). Discuss each of these methods. Which method do the children think would be easier to do? Which method do they think would give more accurate results?
- Discuss the limitations of each method. The first method may not work in a classroom, because it may not be possible to get far enough away for the bulb to be invisible. For the second method, it is important to use sheets of the same type of paper for each bulb, or the comparison will not be a fair one. In both cases, it is very hard to tell at exactly what distance the bulb becomes invisible.
- Ask the children to predict some things that will affect the brightness of bulbs in a circuit, and what effect these things will have.

Children's activity

20–25 mins

- Working in small groups, the children use photocopiable page 87 to record their prediction about how changing the number of batteries in a circuit will affect the brightness of bulbs. They then build a simple series circuit and investigate the effect of changing the number of batteries, measuring brightness by one of the two methods described above and recording their results on page 87.
- They then compare their results with those of another group. Does using one battery always make a bulb have the same brightness? Discuss possible reasons for any differences they find – for example, groups near a window may find that their bulbs appear less bright.

Differentiation

More able: The children could be asked to predict, then test, the effect on brightness of changing the number of bulbs in a circuit.
Less able: The children may need help with deciding how to keep the test fair. Help them to decide what things need to be kept the same throughout the investigation, and to give reasons. They should not compare results with another group, as they may find this confusing.

Links to other topics

Science: Safe use of electricity – why mains electricity and car batteries are dangerous and should not be used in investigations.
Design and technology: Designing and building lights for a model such as a lighthouse, a model car or a model theatre.

HOW CAN WE MEASURE IT?

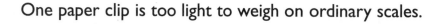

Very small measurements

Finding the mass of a paper clip

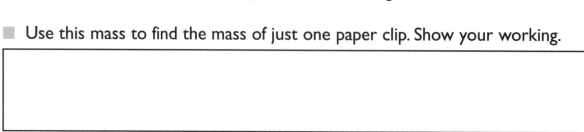

One paper clip is too light to weigh on ordinary scales.

Mass of _____ paper clips = _____ g.

■ Use this mass to find the mass of just one paper clip. Show your working.

```
[                                                                    ]
```

Why is it better to weigh a large number of paper clips rather than just a few?

_____

_____

Finding the thickness of a sheet of paper

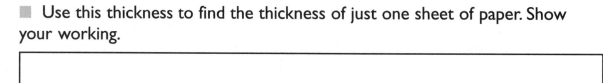

One sheet of paper is too thin to measure with your ruler.

Thickness of _____ sheets of paper = _____ mm.

■ Use this thickness to find the thickness of just one sheet of paper. Show your working.

```
[                                                                    ]
```

Why is it better to measure a large number of sheets rather than just a few?

_____

_____

■ Discuss how you could use measurements of distance and time to compare the smoothness of two slopes.

NOW TRY THIS Can you think of any more 'unusual' things that you could measure using standard units?

How much does one paper clip weigh?

▨ Put one paper clip on your scales.

Reading on scales = _____ g.

Do you think this is the correct mass for one paper clip? _____

▨ Count out 100 paper clips. Weigh them.

Reading on scales = _____ g.

▨ Fill in your readings in this calculation to find the mass of one paper clip.

Mass of one paper clip = mass of 100 paper clips ÷ 100 = _____ g.

Why do you think it is better to weigh 100 paper clips rather than just 5 or 10 paper clips?

_____

_____

_____

HOW CAN WE MEASURE IT?

Which colour shows up best?

The children in Class 6 wanted to know which colour pen they should use to advertise their Class Bring and Buy Sale. They wanted a colour that would show up really well.

■ Discuss what Class 6 mean by 'show up'. Write a question they could test.

_____

_____

■ Describe how you will compare different-coloured pens. Draw a diagram.

What would you do to make sure that your test was a fair comparison?

_____

_____

_____

What things other than the colour would affect how well the Bring and Buy Sale advertisement would show up?

_____

_____

NOW TRY THIS Suggest how you could modify this method to find out which of several torches was working best.

HOW CAN WE MEASURE IT?

Making bulbs brighter and dimmer

■ Draw the circuit you will use to measure the brightness of a bulb.

■ Describe how you will measure how bright the bulb is. You might like to include a drawing.

■ Change the number of batteries in your circuit. Use this table to record how the brightness of the bulb changes.

Number of batteries	How bright the bulb looked	Measurement we recorded

■ Complete this sentence:

Our results told us that _____

_____

NOW TRY THIS Compare your results with another group. Did you get exactly the same results? Can you explain any differences?

SHAPE AND SPACE

WHAT SHAPE IS IT?

MATHS FOCUS: DESCRIBING AND VISUALISING 3-D SHAPES

Learning objectives
- To visualise common 3-D shapes.
- To describe the properties of common 3-D shapes.

Resources
- A board or flip chart, pens.
- A range of common 3-D and 2-D shapes.
- Adhesive tape and/or wipe-clean pens.
- A copy of photocopiable pages 90, 91 and 92 for each child.

Preparation: Photocopy page 91 onto card and cut out the shape cards.

Introduction
5 mins
- Start with a brief reminder of what the children know. Show them some 2-D shapes. Can the children name these shapes? Can they describe them? Show the children some common 3-D shapes. *Who knows what this shape is called? Can you think of anything else that is this shape?*

Whole-class, teacher-directed activity
20 mins
- Show the children a 3-D shape with only flat faces, such as a cube. *If we were describing this shape to someone who was out of the room, what could we tell them?*
- Help the children to describe the shape you have chosen. Introduce and explain the terms *faces, edges* and *vertices. How many **faces** does it have? What shape are they? How many **edges** does it have? How many **vertices** does it have?* Help the children to make definitions of these words. Write them on the board. Use the term *polyhedron* to describe a 3-D shape where every face is a polygon (a flat face with straight sides).
- Display a range of 3-D shapes where all the children can see them. Ask questions such as: *How many faces does this shape have? Can you see a shape with 6 edges? Who can tell me a fact about this shape?*

Children's activity
20–25 mins
- Working individually, the children should complete the table on photocopiable page 90 showing the number of faces, vertices and edges for six common 3-D shapes.
- Working in small groups, the children should play '20 Questions' to identify various 3-D shapes. Each child as 'question master' has a 3-D shape fact card from page 91. The rest of the team ask questions to which the question master can only answer 'Yes' or 'No'. Can they work out what the 3-D shape is?

SCIENCE LINK ACTIVITY

Photocopiable page 92 shows objects that the children can imagine viewing from different directions. They should draw what the object will look like from each view, then swap sheets with a friend and try to identify the object from the three outlines drawn.

Differentiation
These activities should be accessible to children of all abilities. The children may surprise you. Those who are generally more able can sometimes be very poor at visualising 3-D shapes, while children who are generally less able may be very good at this. Some children may enjoy trying to spot Euler's relationship: *faces + vertices = edges + 2.*

Plenary
10 mins
Discuss how easy the children find it to 'picture' 3-D shapes in their heads. If they find it difficult, is it easier to think of the shape as 'like a dice', 'like a Toblerone packet' and so on? Which shapes in the '20 Questions' game were easiest/hardest to guess? Can the children explain why?

SHAPE AND SPACE

SCIENCE FOCUS: HOW WE SEE THINGS (QCA UNIT 6F)

Learning objectives

▪ To identify factors that might affect the size and position of the shadow of an object.
▪ To investigate how changing one factor causes a shadow to change.

Resources

▪ A board or flip chart, pens.
▪ A range of common 3-D shapes.
▪ Torches or other moveable light sources, sheets of white card (or blank walls), a method of dimming the room light.
▪ A copy of photocopiable page 93 for each child.

Introduction

5 mins

▪ Recap on the children's knowledge of shadows. Challenge them to tell you five things they know about shadows. (For example: *You need a light source. The shadow is on the opposite side of the object from the light. The size of a shadow can change. The direction of a shadow can change. Shadows have no colour.*)

Whole-class, teacher-directed activity

15–20 mins

▪ Ask: *Why do objects have shadows?* Encourage the children to draw their ideas on the board. Help them to show clearly that shadows form when something blocks the light coming from a light source. *What shape is the shadow?* (The same shape as the object, because the rays of light travel in straight lines.)
▪ *Can all materials cast shadows?* Show the children that even transparent materials cast a very faint shadow. Explain that this is because transparent objects block a small amount of the light, even though most of it gets through.
▪ Show the children the 3-D shapes. Tell them that they are going to explore ways of changing the shape of the shadow cast by a 3-D shape. Ask them to suggest some ways they might try.

Children's activity

20–25 mins

▪ Working in small groups, the children use photocopiable page 93 to guide their exploration into the shadows cast by different 3-D shapes. First, they choose a 3-D shape and find two ways to make its shadow bigger.
▪ Next, they choose several different 3-D shapes, then make and draw as many different-shaped shadows of it as they can.
▪ Finally, they look at some shadows drawn on page 93, predict what 3-D shape will cast each shadow, then test their prediction.

Differentiation

As with the maths activities on page 88, these activities are accessible to children of all abilities. The children who are best at predicting the shadows cast by the 3-D shapes will not necessarily be those children who are generally more able. In completing the table on page 93, less able children may need help with using a methodical approach to find all the possible different-shaped shadows.

Links to other topics

Literacy/Design and technology: Working as a class to write, stage and produce a 'shadow puppet' play for younger children in the school. **Art:** Using close observation to make pictures with a range of different shadows (for example, varying the 'blackness' of shadows to indicate different levels of sunlight).

SHAPE AND SPACE
PHOTOCOPIABLE

3-D shapes

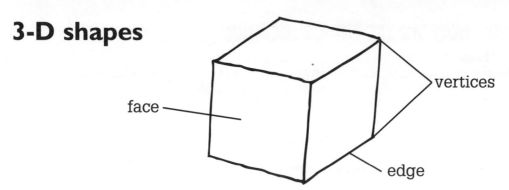

face

vertices

edge

Fill in the table for these common 3-D shapes.

Shape	Number of faces	Number of vertices	Number of edges
Cuboid			
Square-based pyramid			
Tetrahedron			
Triangular prism			
Cone			
Sphere			

NOW TRY THIS Can you find a pattern in the number of faces, vertices and edges for all of these 3-D shapes except the sphere?

3-D shape fact cards

Cuboid

6 faces
4 oblong faces
2 square faces
All faces are flat
12 edges
8 vertices

Square-based pyramid

5 faces
4 triangular faces
1 square face
All faces are flat
8 edges
5 vertices

Tetrahedron

4 faces
4 triangular faces
All faces are flat
6 edges
4 vertices

Triangular prism

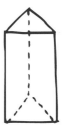

5 faces
2 triangular faces
3 rectangular faces
All faces are flat
9 edges
6 vertices

Cone

2 faces
1 circular face
1 curved face
1 edge
1 vertex

Sphere

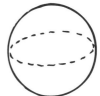

1 face
1 curved face
0 edges
0 vertices

Cube

6 faces
All faces are square
All faces are flat
12 edges
8 vertices

Rhomboid prism (such as a pencil eraser)

6 faces
2 rhomboid faces
4 rectangular faces
All faces are flat
12 edges
8 vertices

WHAT SHAPE IS IT?

The view from here

These children are looking at the same car from different directions.

■ Next to each child, sketch the **outline** of the shape he or she will see.

The model car is replaced with a different object.
These shapes show the **outline** of what each child sees.

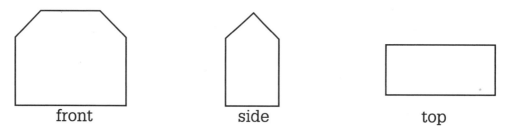

| front | side | top |

What do you think the object is? _____

■ Think of another object. Draw its **outline** from three different directions in the box below. Can your friend work out what your object is?

Changing shadows

■ Choose a 3-D shape to make a shadow.

■ Describe two ways to make the shadow of your shape bigger.

_____

_____

■ Choose three or more 3-D shapes. Write the name of each shape in the table below, then make and draw as many different-shaped shadows with it as you can.

Name of shape	Shadows

■ Look at the shadows below. Predict what 3-D shape they belong to.

MAKING CONNECTIONS

MATHS FOCUS: ORGANISING AND PRESENTING DATA

Learning objective
- Solve a problem by collecting, organising and representing data in tables and line graphs.

Resources
- A board or flip chart, pens.
- A4 graph paper, an A3 copy of resource page 124.
- Metre rulers, weighing scales, stopwatches.
- A graph showing how children's height increases with age (available in most multimedia encyclopedias).
- A copy of photocopiable pages 96 (page 97 for less able children) and 98 for each child.

Introduction
5–10 mins
- Ask the children: *What ways can you record the data you collect?* If necessary, prompt them to think of pictograms, tally charts, Venn diagrams, bar charts and line graphs. Help them to suggest instances when each type of recording would be appropriate.

Whole-class, teacher-directed activity
20–25 mins
- Ask: *How would you collect information to find out what ice cream flavours the children in our school like?* A tally chart will allow them to collect information about several different flavours at once. Use a show of hands to find out which flavours the children in your class like. Record a tally chart on the board.
- Ask: *What would be the best way to present this information?* Plot a class bar chart of preferred flavours on an A3 copy of resource page 124. *How many children are shown on the bar chart? Why is this more children than are in our class?* (Many children like more than one flavour.)
- Remind the children that line graphs are used when two quantities may be related, such as age and height. Show them the height graph and ask them to describe the relationship between height and age, including the rate at which height increases at a given age. *What would the graph look like if there were no connection between height and age?*
- Ask the children to suggest other things that might be connected. *How could you check this? What information would you need to collect? What axes should the graph have?*

Children's activity
20–25 mins
- Photocopiable page 96 lists some pairs of variables that might be connected. Each group should choose two variables, collect data for their group, plot a line graph, then decide whether a connection exists. (Some things listed may not be practical to investigate. Check groups' choices before they collect the data.)

SCIENCE LINK ACTIVITY

Photocopiable page 98 provides two sets of data about a bus journey: one set where there is no connection between the two variables (journey time and day) and another where the two variables (journey time and speed) are connected. The children should decide which to plot as a bar chart and which as a line graph, then suggest other things to represent with bar charts or line graphs.

Differentiation
More able: Can the children think of a relationship where one variable decreases as the other increases? For example: running speed and age; temperature of a cup of hot tea and time.
Less able: The children can use photocopiable page 97 to guide their investigation. Help them to decide what measurements to take, what to plot on the graph, and what scales and units to use.

Plenary
5–10 mins
Encourage the children to describe line graphs for two variables that are connected and two that are not connected.

SCIENCE FOCUS: FORCES IN ACTION (QCA UNIT 6E)

Learning objectives
- To represent data in a line graph and use this to identify patterns in the data.
- To identify appropriate scientific explanations.

Resources
- Sheets of scrap A4 paper, metre rulers.
- A feather, a marble.
- A copy of photocopiable page 99 and a sheet of A4 graph paper for each child.

Introduction
10 mins
- Recap on the children's knowledge of the forces acting on falling objects. Gravity acts downwards, air resistance acts upwards. Show the children a feather and a marble falling. Can they explain why the feather falls more slowly? They should recognise that both the downward force due to gravity (weight) and the air resistance are different.

Whole-class, teacher-directed activity
20–25 mins
- Ask: *How could we do a fair test to find out whether it was air resistance or gravity that made the feather and the marble fall at different speeds?* Emphasise the importance of only changing one thing at once. Show the children three sheets of A4 paper: one unfolded, one folded and one scrunched up. *What has changed here?* Make sure they understand that only the area has changed, not the mass.
- Ask the children to suggest things that might affect how long the paper takes to fall. *Can you predict the effect of changing the area of the paper? How could you test your prediction? What measurements should you take? How should you present the results? What type of line graph do you expect to find if the time to fall is/is not related to the area?*

Children's activity
20–25 mins
- Working in small groups, the children investigate how the area of a sheet of paper affects the time it takes to fall to the ground. They can use page 99 to record their investigation. They should measure the area of the sheet by comparing its size with a sheet of graph paper and counting the squares. They should then plot a graph of time to fall (y-axis) against area (x-axis). They should consider the explanations listed on page 99 and decide which one best explains what they have observed.
  Note: It is not practical to use a stopwatch for this activity, as the times are too short. The children should time by counting as quickly as they can from when the paper is released to when it hits the floor.
- In a plenary session, discuss the possible explanations given on page 99 for the results. Help the children to identify the best explanation (the second one) and decide what is missing or poorly explained in the others. Make sure they understand that a statement is not necessarily a good explanation just because it is true.

Differentiation
More able: Encourage the children to discuss possible ways of improving the investigation. For instance, could the results be made more accurate by using a different method of timing?
Less able: Help the children to decide on the labels and range of numbers for the axes on their graph. Alternatively, give them graph paper with prepared axes.

Links to other topics
Design and technology: Making kites (these need a large area for air resistance, but if the area is too large they fold up and collapse).

MAKING CONNECTIONS

Is it connected?

Children in Class 6 collected lots of information about themselves.

Here are some of the things the children thought might be connected:
- Shoe size and height.
- Height and weight.
- Age and time taken to run across the playground.
- Age and bedtime.

■ Choose **one** of the pairs of variables listed above. Make sure that you will be able to collect enough data for your choice.

■ Find out whether there is a connection for the children in your group or your class.
- What information will you need to collect?
- What will you put on the axes of your line graph?

■ Plot a line graph to show the information you collected.

■ What does your graph show?

_____

_____

_____

NOW TRY THIS Can you think of any pairs of variables where one variable goes down as the other one goes up?

Is it connected?

The children in Class 6 collected lots of information about themselves.

Here are some of the things the children thought might be connected:
- Shoe size and height.
- Height and results in spelling tests.
- Height and weight.

▪ Choose **one** pair of variables that you think are connected.
▪ Collect measurements of these two things for your group.
▪ Plot a line graph. Your teacher will tell you what axes to use.
▪ Compare your graph with these:

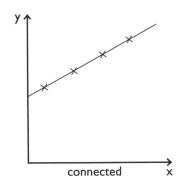
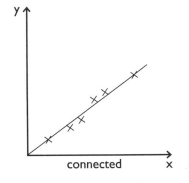
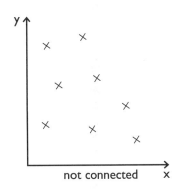

Do you think your two variables are connected? _____
▪ Explain why.

_____

_____

_____

MAKING CONNECTIONS

Line graph or bar chart?

The tables below show two sets of information about a bus journey.

Day	Journey time in minutes
Monday	6
Tuesday	8
Wednesday	12
Thursday	8
Friday	8

Average speed of bus (km/h)	Journey time (min)
8	30
16	15
24	10
32	8
40	6

Which set of information would you use a bar chart to represent? Why?

_____

_____

Which set of information would you use a line graph to represent? Why?

_____

_____

■ Plot each journey on graph paper, using the appropriate type of graph.

 NOW TRY THIS Suggest another set of data you could represent with a bar chart, and another set you could represent with a line graph.

Battle of the forces

▨ This falling sheet of paper has two forces acting on it.

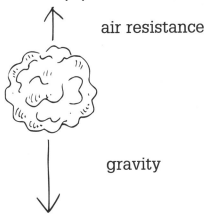

air resistance

gravity

▨ Find out how the area of the paper affects how long it takes to fall.

Area of paper in squares	Time to fall (by counting)

▨ Plot a line graph of time to fall (y-axis) against area (x-axis).

Which of these is the best explanation for your results?

- It's because of air resistance.
- The unfolded sheet traps more air, so there is a bigger force of air resistance pushing up against gravity, so the sheet takes longer to fall.
- The big sheet floats in air because air holds it up.
- The flat sheet falls slowest.
- The scrunched-up paper falls faster than the unfolded sheet.
- Real parachutes are big to make the person come down slowly.

NOW TRY THIS Can you think of any ways to improve your investigation?

USING PIE CHARTS

MATHS FOCUS: INTERPRETING AND MAKING PIE CHARTS

Learning objectives
- To solve a problem by collecting and organising data.
- To begin to interpret simple pie charts.

Resources
- Different-coloured card sectors to cover ½, ¼, ¾, ⅛, ⅓ and ⅔ of a circle, Blu-tack.
- A copy of photocopiable pages 102 (page 103 for less able children), 104 and resource page 125 for each child; an A3 copy of resource page 126.

Introduction
5 mins
- Use Blu-tack to display an A3 copy of resource page 125 where the class can see it. Hold up the different-sized card sectors. *What fraction of a circle is this? How many of these would fit in a whole circle? What other piece could I add to this one to make a complete circle?*
- Recap on any knowledge the children have about pie charts. Pie charts are a way of showing a proportion as well as a number – for example, the fractions of children in the class who like different ice cream flavours.

Whole-class, teacher-directed activity
20–25 mins
- Tell the children: *We are going to make pie charts to show things that you like.* Direct the children's attention to the A3 copy of resource page 125. *This circle represents all the children in our class. How many of you have pets?* Ask the children to estimate the fraction of the class that have pets. *Which card sector should we use to represent the children who have pets?* Place the appropriate sector over the large circle. Repeat with other examples.
- Use the ¼ and ⅓ sectors to make a pie chart with one sector uncovered. Tell the children: *The whole of this pie chart represents a class of 24 children. The [colour of ¼ sector] represents the children who walk to school. Who can tell me how many children walk to school?* Repeat with the coloured card for the ⅓ section, then repeat with other pie charts.

Children's activity
20–25 mins
- The children work individually or in pairs to complete photocopiable page 102. This contains pie charts with accompanying questions and information that the children can use to draw their own pie chart. (Answers: **1** B, **2** C, **3** 25, **4** 300.)
- They should then work in pairs to invent a pie chart of their own, using resource page 125 (one sector can represent each child in a class of 30). Each pair should describe to another pair what their pie chart shows. For example, 'Our pie chart shows that ¾ of the children in our class have their own pencil cases.'

SCIENCE LINK ACTIVITY

Give the children individual copies of photocopiable page 104. They should use the pie charts (which represent data from a 'real life' situation) to compare how well bean plants grow in two different places. They can go on to explain the results (the soil under the tree has less light, and perhaps fewer nutrients, than the soil in the vegetable patch).

Differentiation
More able: Encourage the children to ask each other questions about the pie charts they invent, such as: *What fraction of the children does this section of the pie chart represent? How many children is that?*
Less able: The children could complete photocopiable page 103, which contains similar tasks to page 102 but uses the fractions ¼, ½ and ¾ only. (Answers: **1** ½, **2** ¼, **3** 50, **4.** 200.)

Plenary
10 mins
Ask some of the children to show and describe the pie charts they have created. Encourage other children to ask them questions.

SCIENCE FOCUS: INTERDEPENDENCE AND ADAPTATION (QCA UNIT 6A)

Learning objectives
- To know that fertilisers can be added to soils to provide nutrients for plant growth.
- To know that the quantities of fertiliser needed are very small.

Resources
- A tray of seedlings for each group (fast-growing seedlings such as cress are ideal), 15cm or 30cm rulers marked in mm.
- Ready-mixed liquid plant fertiliser (one solution at recommended strength, one solution at three times recommended strength), packaging from a range of plant fertilisers.
- A copy of photocopiable page 105 for each child.

Safety: Children should not handle fertilisers. They should water their seedlings with plant food already prepared to the correct concentration and measured out to the correct volume.

Introduction
5 mins
- Review the things that plants need to make them grow well. Use questions such as: *What happens if we don't water a plant? What happens if we put it in the dark? What happens if we cut off the leaves?* Establish that plants need light, water, warmth and healthy roots, stems and leaves in order to grow well.

Whole-class, teacher-directed activity
10 mins
- Show the children the fertiliser packaging. *What is fertiliser for?* Discuss the amount of 'plant food' given to plants and how it compares with the amount of food eaten by animals. Establish that fertilisers are not 'food' for plants: they are chemicals that improve a plant's ability to make its own food from water and light.
- Show the children the trays of seedlings. Discuss ways of using these to investigate the effect of fertilisers on plant growth.
- Discuss how the investigation can be made fair. *What should we change?* (The amount of fertiliser). *What should we keep the same?* (The amounts of water, light and warmth.)
- Discuss how pie charts can be used to show the proportions of tall, short and medium seedlings. The children should understand that it is not necessary to count and measure all the seedlings, only to estimate the fraction (such as $1/4$) above or below a chosen height.

Children's activity
20–25 mins
- The children use photocopiable page 105 to record a prediction about the effect of fertiliser on plant growth. Working in small groups, they measure some of their seedlings and estimate an 'original height' that ¾ of the seedlings are below. They complete a simple pie chart on page 105 to record this.
- The children keep their tray of seedlings moist with either water or one of the solutions of fertiliser. Make sure that roughly equal numbers of groups use water and the two solutions.
- After two weeks they should measure their seedlings, estimating the proportion that are below the 'original height' and the proportions at taller heights (see 'Differentiation'). They should record these results on a second pie chart.
- A plenary discussion can be used to establish which sets of seedlings have grown best. (The seedlings watered with the recommended solution of fertiliser will have grown best.)

Differentiation
More able: Encourage the children to be as accurate as possible in their measuring and estimating, dividing their 'results' pie chart into sectors for three, or even four, different heights.
Less able: The children should divide their 'results' pie charts into just two sectors, showing the proportions of seedlings above and below the 'original' height.

Links to other topics
Geography: Identifying the suitability of different soils for farming.
History: Relating the locations of settlements to the fertility of soil in different regions.

USING PIE CHARTS

Pie charts

These three pie charts show how children in different areas travel to school.

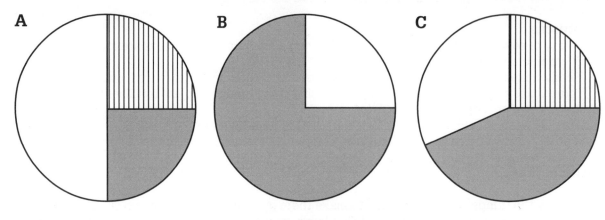

A   B   C

Key

 walk to school

 travel by car

 travel by bus

1. School 1 is in a rural area with no buses.
Which pie chart represents School 1?   _____

2. ⅓ of the children at School 2 walk to school.
Which pie chart represents School 2?   _____

3. Pie chart B represents 100 children.
How many of these children walk to school?   _____

4. Pie chart A represents School 3. 150 children at School 3
walk to school. How many children go to School 3?   _____

■ On the back of this sheet, draw a pie chart for School 4.
Use this information:
- 240 children attend School 4.
- ⅓ of the children travel to school by bus.
- 60 children walk to school.

NOW TRY THIS   How many children at School 4 travel to school by car?

Pie charts

This pie chart shows how the children at a particular school travel to it.

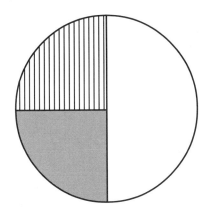

Key

☐ walk

▥ bus

▦ car

1. What fraction of the children walk to school? _____

2. What fraction of the children travel by bus? _____

3. 50 children travel by car. How many children travel by bus? _____

4. How many children are there in the school? _____

■ Draw a pie chart for a school where ¾ of the children walk to school and ¼ travel by car.

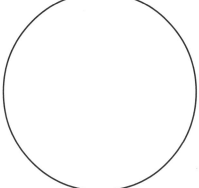

■ Draw a pie chart for a school with 80 children where 40 of them walk to school, 20 travel by bus and 20 travel by car.

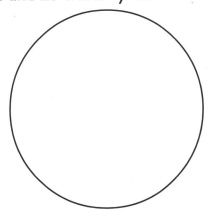

USING PIE CHARTS

Where do bean plants grow best?

Jo grew bean plants in two different places. There were 8 bean plants in each place.

In the vegetable patch   Under a large tree

This pie chart shows how many beans grew on the plants under the tree.

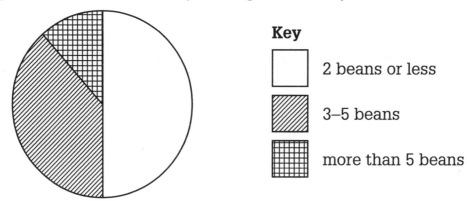

Key

☐ 2 beans or less

▨ 3–5 beans

▦ more than 5 beans

How many plants had 2 beans or less? _____

■ Draw a pie chart for the plants in the vegetable patch. Use this information:
  ■ 5 plants had more than 5 beans.
  ■ 3 plants had 3–5 beans.

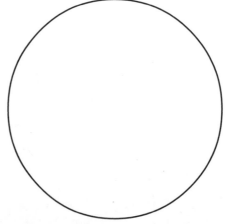

NOW TRY THIS   Which place is better for growing bean plants?
Can you suggest a reason why?

RECORDING AND ORGANISING DATA

USING PIE CHARTS

How does fertiliser affect plants?

▧ Predict how adding fertiliser to soil will affect growing seedlings.

_____

_____

▧ Describe your investigation. You might like to include a diagram.

Results: We estimated that ¾ of our seedlings were shorter than _____ cm.

▧ Show your results
on a pie chart. Make
up your own key.

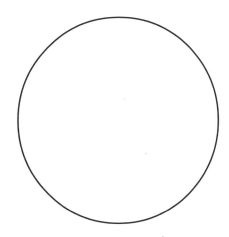

What did you water your seedlings with? _____

▧ Draw a pie chart to
show the heights of your
seedlings after 2 weeks.

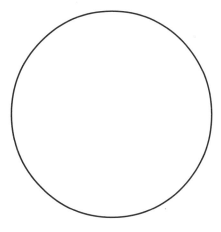

What conclusion can you draw about the effect of fertiliser on plant growth?

_____

_____

THE VALUES IN BETWEEN

MATHS FOCUS: DRAWING AND INTERPRETING LINE GRAPHS

Learning objective
■ To begin to draw and interpret a line graph in which intermediate values have meaning.

Resources
■ A set of standard masses (up to 700g in 100g units), rulers.
■ Force meters (capable of reading up to 10N in 1N units), bathroom scales reading in kg.
■ A copy for each child of photocopiable pages 108 (page 109 for less able children) and 110 for each child; graph paper (A4 for children, plus one enlarged to A3).

Introduction
5–10 mins
■ Explain to the children that they are going to solve problems by drawing and reading line graphs. Recap on the important features of a line graph. It must have a title and labelled axes with an appropriate scale. The best scale is found by looking at the largest and smallest readings and choosing the scale that will best fill the space available. The line drawn may be a jagged line connecting all the points (as in a patient's temperature graph), or it may be the (straight or curved) line of 'best fit' through the points. Show a few examples, such as a graph of children's height against weight (straight line of best fit) and a graph of temperature against time for a cup of tea (curve of best fit).

Whole-class, teacher-directed activity
20–25 mins
■ Say: *The Brown family are going on holiday to France. They know France uses euros, and they need to know how much they will be able to buy with their money when they get there. The exchange rate says that £100 = €150. How could we draw a graph to show them how to change pounds to euros?*
■ Help the children to draw the axes (use graph paper set as landscape, with euros along the x-axis and pounds up the y-axis), plot points (discuss suitable points, such as £0 = €0, £100 = €150, £200 = €300) and draw a straight line through them as far as the axes will allow. Explain that the graph can convert any amount from one currency to the other.
■ Use the graph to solve problems together, such as: *A hotel room for their stay will cost €450. How many pounds is this? The Brown children have £50 spending money. How many euros is that?* As an extension, try: *If the Browns started out with £1000 and spent €1200, how many pounds did they have when they came home?*

Children's activity
20–25 mins
■ The children should use photocopiable page 108 to plot a graph showing the speed conversion from mph to km/h. They use this graph to answer questions, including ones about intermediate points they have not plotted.

SCIENCE LINK ACTIVITY

The children use standard masses and force meters to find the numerical relationship between mass in grams and weight in newtons. They record their results on photocopiable page 110, then plot a graph showing the conversion and extend the line to find out how many newtons a mass of 1kg will weigh.

Differentiation
More able: Can the children work together to define the relationship between miles and km? (1 mile = 1.6km)
Less able: Children can complete page 109, which only asks questions about points marked on the graph (except for the 'Now try this' activity). You could provide graph paper with prepared axes.

Plenary
10 mins
Ask some children to explain how they used their graphs to answer some of the questions. Discuss whether these conversion graphs (pounds to euros and mph to km/h) would be useful to a French family holidaying in the UK.

THE VALUES IN BETWEEN

SCIENCE FOCUS: FORCES IN ACTION (QCA UNIT 6E)

Learning objectives
- To represent data in a line graph and use this to identify patterns in the data.
- To know that how much an elastic band stretches depends on the force acting on it.

Resources
- Elastic bands, standard masses (up to 600g for each group, in units of 100g), rulers marked in millimetres.
- A copy of photocopiable page 111 and a sheet of A4 graph paper for each child.

Safety: Refer to your LEA/school safety guidelines. If you use strong elastic bands such as those used to fasten bundles of post, and masses of no more than 700g, the risk of elastic bands snapping and dropping the masses is minimal.

Introduction
5–10 mins
- Discuss the children's knowledge of how elastic bands stretch. Can they identify the forces involved and the directions the forces act in? Elastic bands only stretch when they are pulled: the force within the stretched elastic band means that it will return to its original shape when released. This is why elastic bands are good at holding things together: a stretched elastic band maintains a constant pull.

Whole-class, teacher-directed activity
20 mins
- Pass an elastic band to a child, saying: *Stretch it a little bit.* Give it to another child, saying: *Stretch it more.* (Make sure they do not risk snapping it.) Ask each child to explain how he or she made the band stretch the amount you asked. Ask the children whether there is a connection between the force used and the distance the band stretches. Can they predict how the two will be related?
- Discuss how the children could investigate their prediction. *What will you have to do? What will you have to change? What will you have to measure? What will be the best way to present the results?* If necessary, remind them of the line graphs they have drawn to show the relationship between pounds and euros, or between mph and km/h.
- Explain that when we measure how much the elastic band has stretched, we are measuring how much longer it has become – so we could record and plot a graph of length instead of 'amount of stretch'. Discuss why measuring the length is easier than measuring how far the band has stretched: we do not have to subtract the length of the unstretched band.

Children's activity
20–25 mins
- Working in small groups, the children hang different standard masses (from 200g to 600g) on an elastic band and measure its length each time. They can use photocopiable page 111 to record their results.
- Using either the conversion graph from the 'Science Link' activity or a prepared mass (g) to weight (N) conversion table, the children should plot a line graph to show the length of the elastic band (y-axis) against the force applied (x-axis). They should be able to draw the straight line of best fit, showing that the relationship between force applied and stretch is a constant one within this range. They can then use their graph to answer the questions on photocopiable page 111.

Differentiation
More able: Can the children predict what the line graph might look like for a stronger or weaker elastic band?
Less able: Help the children to decide on suitable labels for the graph axes and a suitable range of numbers on each axis. If necessary, help them to draw the straight line of best fit.

Links to other topics
Citizenship: Discussing the concern for their own and others' safety when carrying out experiments such as this one.

THE VALUES IN BETWEEN

The Browns' holiday in France

The speedometer in the Browns' car measures speed in miles per hour. Speed limits in France are shown in kilometres per hour.

Speed in miles per hour (mph)	Speed in kilometres per hour (km/h)
0	0
25	40
50	80
75	120
100	160

■ Use the information in the table to plot a graph showing the conversion of speed in miles per hour to speed in kilometres per hour.

■ Use your graph to answer these questions.

1. What would a speed limit of 70mph be to the nearest 10km/h? _____

2. A sign in France gives the speed limit as 100km/h.
What is this in mph to the nearest 5mph?   _____

3. The speed limit near a French school is 30km/h.
What is this in mph to the nearest 5mph?   _____

■ Answer the following questions.
Travelling at 50mph, the Browns take 1 hour to complete a journey.

■ How long was the journey in miles? _____

■ What was their average speed in km/h? _____

■ How long was the journey in kilometres? _____

■ Can you write the relationship between distance in miles and in kilometres?

_____

The Browns' holiday in France

The speedometer in the Browns' car measures speed in miles per hour. Speed limits in France are shown in kilometres per hour.

Speed in miles per hour (mph)	Speed in kilometres per hour (km/h)
0	0
25	40
50	80
75	120
100	160

▓ Use the information in the table to plot a graph of speed in miles per hour (on the y-axis) against speed in kilometres per hour (on the x-axis).

▓ Use your graph to answer these questions.

1. How fast would the Browns be travelling, in km/h, if their speedometer read 75mph? _____

2. A speed limit sign reads 80km/h. How fast is this in mph? _____

NOW TRY THIS

The speed limit near a French school is 30km/h.
What is this in mph to the nearest 5mph?

THE VALUES IN BETWEEN

Mass and weight

The mass of an object is a measure of how much matter it contains. Mass is measured in grams (g). The weight of an object is a measure of the force of gravity exerted on it by the Earth. All forces are measured in newtons (N).

Because there is a constant relationship between mass and weight near the Earth's surface, we can use scales (which really measure weight) to tell us the mass of an object. We often say that this mass is the object's 'weight'.

■ Hang standard masses from 100g to 700g on a force meter.

■ Use the table below to record the force meter readings.

Mass in grams	100	200	300	400	500	600	700
Weight in newtons							

■ Plot a graph to show the relationship between grams and newtons. You will need to use the following labels on the axes:

■ Show newtons on the y-axis. Adjust your scale to use only about two thirds of the height of the graph paper with the values you have measured.

■ Show grams on the x-axis. Use values from 0g to 1200g.

1. Use your graph to convert 1kg into newtons. _____

2. Use bathroom scales to find your **mass** to the nearest 1kg. _____

3. Calculate your **weight** in newtons.

_____

_____

Stretching an elastic band

■ Measure how long your elastic band is when different standard masses are hung from it. Use values of mass up to 800g.

■ Record your results in this table. Complete the table by finding the weight (in newtons) that corresponds to each value of mass (in grams).

Mass (g)	Force (N)	Length (mm)

■ Plot a graph to show the length of the elastic band (y-axis) against the **force** applied to stretch it (x-axis).

■ Use your graph to answer these questions.

1. How long was your elastic band
when a force of 5N was applied to it? _____

2. What length would your elastic band
be if a mass of 800g were hung on it? _____

3. What length would your elastic band
be if no force was applied to stretch it? _____

■ Write a conclusion to explain the relationship between the length of the elastic band and the force applied to it.

_____

_____

_____

SOLVING AND DISSOLVING

MATHS FOCUS: DRAWING AND INTERPRETING LINE GRAPHS

Learning objective
■ To solve a problem by interpreting data in a line graph.

Resources
■ Graph paper (A4 for the children, one sheet enlarged to A3), rulers.
■ A copy of photocopiable page 114 (page 115 for less able children) and 116 for each child.

Introduction
5–10 mins
■ Ask: *What happens to your height as you get older? How can we present measurements of height and age to show the relationship?* Discuss the children's suggestions.
■ Discuss how to represent the table below as a graph. Remind the children of the important features of a graph: it must have a title; the numbers on each axis must increase regularly; they usually (not always) start at 0; the value being changed in a regular way goes on the x-axis; the variable being measured goes on the y-axis.

Age (years)	2	4	6	8	10	12	14	16
Height (cm)	85	100	115	125	135	145	160	175

Whole-class, teacher-directed activity
15–20 mins
■ Make a class graph of height against age. Use A4, standard 1cm graph paper enlarged to A3 in 'portrait' layout.
■ Help the children to decide which set of data goes on each axis. (x-axis: age from 0 to 16 years; y-axis: height from 0 to 180cm.) More able children will see that plotting height from 80cm to 180cm gives a graph that is easier to read values from. Label the axes.
■ Ask individual children to plot points on the graph, and others to check these. Decide how to draw the line. *Should this be a straight line?* (No, because the graph shows three distinct phases of growth: the growth rate is not constant.)
■ Use the graph to answer questions, such as: *How tall was the child at age 15? How tall was the child when she was born? How tall will she be at age 18? How tall will this person be at age 30?* (The last two questions require the children to use their knowledge of the pattern of human growth.)

SCIENCE LINK ACTIVITY

Photocopiable page 116 provides data on the time taken to dissolve two different brands of sweetener at four different temperatures. The children should plot a graph showing time to dissolve against temperature of water, with a separate line for each sweetener. They can use this graph to decide which sweetener would be better for hot drinks, and which would be better for cold drinks.

Children's activity
20–25 mins
■ The children use photocopiable page 114 to plot a graph showing the amount of sugar needed to make different numbers of biscuits. They should then use the graph to answer the questions in Set A (reading from the graph) and Set B (estimating unplotted values).

Differentiation
More able: Ask the children to draw another line on the graph, showing the amount of porridge oats used in different numbers of biscuits (the recipe uses twice as much sugar as porridge oats).
Less able: The children could plot their graph using the prepared axes on photocopiable page 115. They could answer only the questions in Set A on page 114.

Plenary
10 mins
Look at the graphs the children have drawn. Discuss the children's answers to the questions on page 114.

SOLVING AND DISSOLVING

SCIENCE FOCUS: MORE ABOUT DISSOLVING (QCA UNIT 6C)

Learning objectives
- To plan and carry out a fair test.
- To use a line graph to present results.

Resources
- Large containers of water at four temperatures: 0°C (from the freezer), 20°C (room temperature), 40°C (warm), 60°C (hot). Label the containers with the temperatures and add hot or chilled water as necessary to keep the temperatures approximately constant.
- Beakers, measuring jugs, packaged synthetic sweeteners, white sugar, brown sugar crystals (as used in restaurants), spoons or stirrers.
- A copy of photocopiable page 117 and a sheet of A4 graph paper for each child.

Safety: Care should be taken when handling hot water. 60°C is about the temperature of most domestic hot water taps. Supervise the children's investigation closely.

Introduction
10 mins
- Recap on what the children know about dissolving. *Name some substances that dissolve in water. How does sugar make drinks sweet? Can you explain what is happening when a substance dissolves?*

Whole-class, teacher-directed activity
10–15 mins
- Ask: *Do all things dissolve equally easily?* Discuss their ideas, then dissolve some white sugar and some brown sugar crystals in water at room temperature. (The brown crystals will dissolve much more slowly.) Ask the children what factors might affect how quickly something dissolves. Record their ideas.
- Show the children some packaged synthetic sweeteners. Ask: *Who knows what these are for?* Tell the children that the manufacturer needs to know whether the sweetener takes the same time to dissolve in hot and in cold drinks. *How could we find out?* They will need to measure the time the sweetener takes to dissolve at different temperatures.
- Discuss ways of making the investigation fair. *What needs to be changed?* (The temperature of the water.) *What needs to be kept the same?* (The amount of water, the amount of sweetener, how much it is stirred.)
- Talk about ways of making the results more reliable. (Take two or three readings of the time for the sweetener to dissolve at each temperature.) The children may need to be reminded to use fresh water each time.

Children's activity
20–25 mins
- Working in small groups, the children use photocopiable page 117 to plan and carry out an investigation into how temperature affects the time that a sweetener takes to dissolve. They should take three readings at each temperature and calculate an average, then plot a graph of time against temperature and use it to draw a conclusion.

Differentiation
More able: The children can extend the line they have drawn on their graph to estimate the time the sweetener would take to dissolve in coffee at 100°C. Ask them to write a sentence to explain what they did to make sure their results were as reliable as possible.
Less able: Help the children to decide on labels for the graph axes and the range of numbers on each axis. Ask them to plot the middle value of their three readings on the graph.

Links to other topics
Science: Healthy eating – the relative advantages of sugar (more calories for activity) and synthetic sweetener (does not cause tooth decay).
Design and technology: Designing attractive and convenient packaging for sweeteners, including an opening that provides one tablet at a time; designing posters or leaflets to advertise a sweetener.

SOLVING AND DISSOLVING

Making biscuits

This table shows how much sugar Mrs Kay uses to make her biscuits.

Number of biscuits	Amount of sugar (grams)
20	100
40	200
60	300
80	400
100	500
120	600

■ Plot a graph of the amount of sugar used against the number of biscuits made. Remember to give your graph a title and label the axes.

■ Use your graph to answer these questions.

Set A

1. What is shown on the x-axis? _____

2. How much sugar is needed to make 60 biscuits? _____

3. How many biscuits could Mrs Kay make with 500g of sugar? _____

Set B

1. How much sugar is needed to make 50 biscuits? _____

2. How many biscuits could Mrs Kay make with 25g of sugar? _____

NOW TRY THIS Mrs Kay uses twice as much sugar as porridge oats. Draw a line on the graph to show what amount of porridge oats she uses in her biscuits.

Graph sheet for making biscuits

Graph of _____

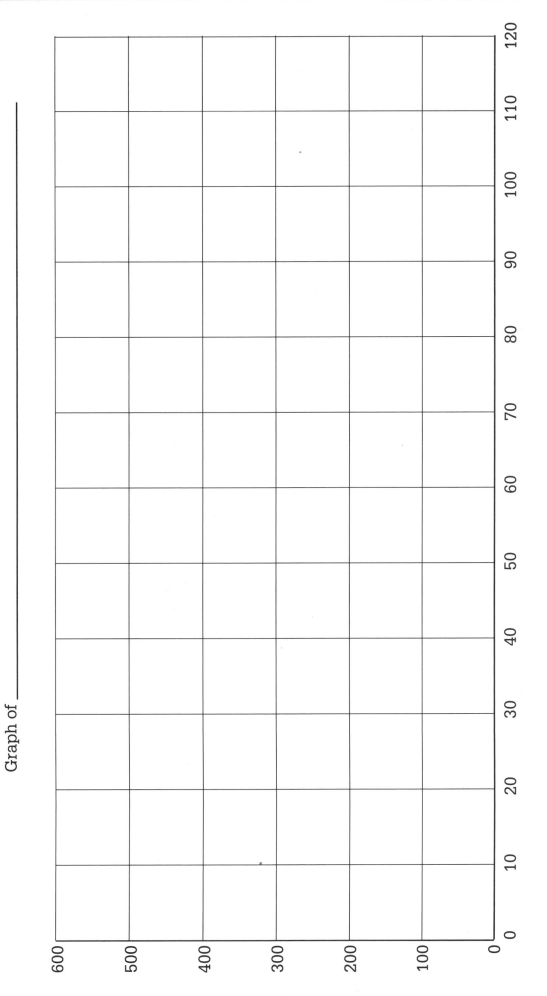

SOLVING AND DISSOLVING

Which sweetener is better?

The children in Class 6 tested two new brands of sweetener, 'Oh So Sweet' and 'Just Like Sugar'.

Here are their results.

Water temperature (°C)	Time taken to dissolve (s)	
	'Oh So Sweet'	'Just Like Sugar'
0	4.5	6
20	4	5
40	3.5	4
60	3	3

■ For 'Oh So Sweet', plot a graph of the time taken to dissolve (y-axis) against the water temperature (x-axis). Use these values for the axes:
  ■ x-axis 0 to 100°C
  ■ y-axis 0 to 6 seconds.

■ Draw the line and continue it to 100°C. Label it 'Oh So Sweet'.

■ On the same axes, plot a graph of the time taken to dissolve against the water temperature for 'Just Like Sugar'.

■ Draw the line and continue it to 100°C. Label it 'Just Like Sugar'.

■ Complete these sentences:

At _____ both sweeteners take the same time to dissolve.

At 80°C, 'Oh So Sweet' takes _____ to dissolve.

When 'Just Like Sugar' takes 4.5s to dissolve, the temperature is

_____ °C.

NOW TRY THIS Which sweetener would you put in hot drinks? Why? Which would you put in cold drinks?

MATHS SKILLS FOR SCIENCE: YEARS 5&6

How fast does a sweetener dissolve?

■ Plan an investigation into how temperature affects the time a sweetener takes to dissolve.

What will you do? What will you measure? (Keep your answers short.)

_____

_____

_____

How will you make sure it is a fair test?

_____

_____

_____

■ Carry out your investigation. Record your results in this table.

Water temperature (°C)	Time taken for sweetener to dissolve (s)			
	1st reading	2nd reading	3rd reading	Average

■ Plot a graph of the time the sweetener takes to dissolve (y-axis) against the water temperature (x-axis).

■ Complete this conclusion:

The graph tells us that _____

_____

_____

NOW TRY THIS

How long do you think your sweetener would take to dissolve in black coffee made with water at 100°C?

HANDLING AND INTERPRETING DATA

GET IT SORTED!

MATHS FOCUS: DRAWING AND INTERPRETING CARROLL DIAGRAMS

Learning objectives
- Solve a problem by collecting and sorting data.
- Use sorting diagrams to display information about shapes or numbers.

Resources
- A board or flip chart, pens.
- A selection of card or plastic rectangles and triangles in two different colours, Blu-tack.
- A copy of photocopiable pages 120 (page 121 for less able children) and 122 for each child.

Introduction
5 mins
- Recap on what the children know about Carroll diagrams. They may not have used them since Year 4. Remind them that Carroll diagrams are used to sort things by two criteria at once – for instance, sorting minibeasts by number of legs and whether they have wings.

Whole-class, teacher-directed activity
20 mins
- Draw a large, unlabelled Carroll diagram (similar to those on pages 120 and 121) on the board. Attach your card or plastic shapes to the diagram, sorted according to shape and colour. Ask the children to identify the criteria you have used for sorting – they should find this quite easy. Label the Carroll diagram.
- Draw another Carroll diagram. Ask the children to suggest criteria that could be used to sort numbers (for example, 'even number' and 'multiple of 7)'. Label the diagram and ask the children for numbers that could go in each section. Ask them to justify their choices. Repeat with progressively more challenging criteria.
- Draw a Carroll diagram for numbers, sorting according to criteria that you have not yet used. Can the children identify the criteria you are using?

Children's activity
20–25 mins
- The children work individually or in pairs to complete photocopiable page 120. This sheet provides a labelled Carroll diagram where the sorting criteria are *factors of 36* or *not factors of 36* and *square numbers* or *not square numbers*. The children should use these criteria to sort the selection of numbers provided and write them in the correct sections of the Carroll diagram. Give them a second selection of numbers and ask to choose appropriate sorting criteria. Examples of appropriate criteria might be *multiples of 3* or *not multiples of 3* and *multiples of 5* or *not multiples of 5*.

SCIENCE LINK ACTIVITY

Photocopiable page 122 presents pictures of a variety of animals for the children to group in a Carroll diagram, according to the criteria *live in the sea* or *not live in the sea* and *mammals* or *not mammals*. They then work in pairs to draw their own Carroll diagrams for a set of animals (of their own choice) and ask another pair to decide what sorting criteria they have used.

Differentiation
More able: Encourage the children to think of more Carroll diagrams, with at least one of the criteria being 'factors of…' (a chosen number). They should choose an appropriate set of numbers to match their criteria.

Less able: The children could complete photocopiable page 121, which requires them only to sort numbers according to what they are multiples of. A partly labelled Carroll diagram is provided for the activity in which the children choose the sorting criteria.

Plenary
10 mins
Check that the children have grouped the numbers correctly in the Carroll diagrams on pages 120 and 121. Discuss other situations in which Carroll diagrams might be used – for example, sorting biscuits according to whether they are suitable for special diets such as *nut allergy* and *egg allergy*.

GET IT SORTED!

SCIENCE FOCUS: INTERDEPENDENCE AND ADAPTATION (QCA UNIT 6A)

Learning objectives
■ To look at how plants in a local habitat are suited to their environment.
■ To look at some ways in which plants and animals are interdependent.

Resources
■ A board or flip chart, pens.
■ Pictures of a range of different plants (including roots and fruits where possible) growing in a range of different habitats.
■ A copy of photocopiable page 123 for each child.

Introduction
5 mins
■ Ask: *Are all plants the same? Do all plants grow in the same kind of environment?* Discuss why different plants grow in different places. Make sure all the children understand that the plants that grow naturally in any habitat are the ones that are suited to that particular set of conditions.

Whole-class, teacher-directed activity
15–20 mins
■ Consider some of the ways in which different plants are adapted to live in conditions that are particularly dry, wet, hot or cold. Draw on the children's knowledge to consider how different types of fruit formation or seed dispersal are adaptations to the conditions in which the plants live. For example, it would not be effective for a plant living in woodland undergrowth to rely on wind dispersal for its seeds.
■ Discuss ways in which some plants depend on animals, or try to protect themselves from animals. Discuss what the plants stand to gain or to lose from their contact with animals. For instance, it is worthwhile for some plants to use energy in producing a fruit that animals will eat so that the animals will disperse their seeds in another area. Other plants produce thorns or unpleasant flavours in order to prevent animals from eating their leaves or stems.
■ Explain that the ways in which plants are adapted to their environment are often very complicated. This makes protecting endangered species difficult, because scientists do not really understand all the ways in which the endangered species depend on their surroundings. However, it is sometimes possible to use a Carroll diagram to draw simple conclusions about some of the ways in which plants are adapted to their surroundings.

Children's activity
20–25 mins
■ Working in pairs or small groups, the children use the Carroll diagram on photocopiable page 123 to group the plants shown according to whether they store food in their roots and whether they produce a fruit intended for animals to eat. The children should draw the conclusion from the completed Carroll diagram that some plants use energy to attract animals that will help to disperse their seeds, and other plants store energy in their roots to use later, but no plants do both.

Differentiation
More able: Encourage the children to make a list of plants that depend on animals and, for each plant, to describe what the plants gain from the relationship. Do the animals gain anything from it?
Less able: Ask the children to think of two more plants that might fit into the Carroll diagram and to add them to the correct section(s).

Links to other topics
Citizenship: Protecting the environment. The children could consider the relative merits of conflicting designs for the use of a given area of land, taking into account human and environmental concerns. **Art:** Using dried fruits and seeds for collage work.

GET IT SORTED!

Sorting numbers using Carroll diagrams

■ Write the numbers below in the correct sections of this Carroll diagram.

	Factors of 36	Not factors of 36
Square numbers		
Not square numbers		

2	3	4	5	6	7
8	9	10	11	12	15
16	18	20	24	25	30

■ Look at this selection of numbers.

5	6	8	9	10	12
14	15	16	18	19	20
21	24	25	27	30	35

■ Choose two appropriate sorting criteria for these numbers. Make a Carroll diagram for the numbers on another sheet of paper.

NOW TRY THIS
Make another Carroll diagram where one of the sorting criteria is 'factors of...' (a number you have chosen).

MATHS SKILLS FOR SCIENCE: YEARS 5&6

GET IT SORTED!

Sorting numbers using Carroll diagrams

▨ Write the numbers below in the correct places in this Carroll diagram.

	Multiples of 10	Not multiples of 10
Multiples of 4		
Not multiples of 4		

4	8	10	11	12	15
16	19	20	24	25	30
32	40	50	150	160	200

▨ Use your completed Carroll diagram to list all the numbers that are multiples of 4 **and** 10.

▨ Look at this selection of numbers.

5	6	8	9	10	12
14	15	16	18	19	20
21	24	25	27	30	35

▨ On another sheet of paper, make a Carroll diagram and put these numbers into it. Use 'multiples of 3' or 'not multiples of 3' as one criterion. Choose your own second criterion.

GET IT SORTED!

Using a Carroll diagram to sort animals

■ Sort these animals by writing their names in the Carroll diagram below.

	Live in the sea	Do not live in the sea
Mammals		
Not mammals		

■ Make up your own Carroll diagram to sort animals, using a set of animals that you have chosen. Don't label your sorting criteria. Can another group work out what criteria you have used?

Using a Carroll diagram to sort plants

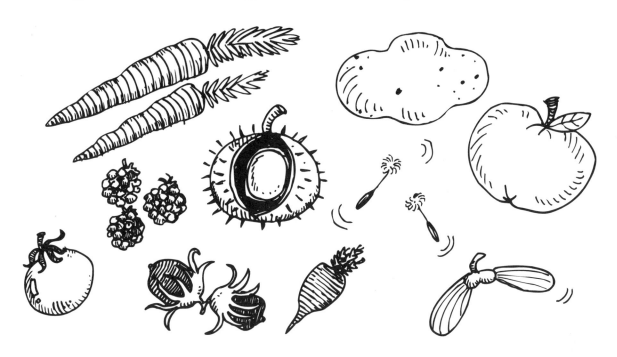

▧ Sort these plants into the following Carroll diagram.

	Stores food in its roots	Does not store food in its roots
Fruit intended for animals to eat		
Fruit not intended for animals to eat		

What conclusion can you draw from this Carroll diagram?

NOW TRY THIS Make a list of plants that depend on animals. In each case, say what the plant gains from the relationship.

Name

Date

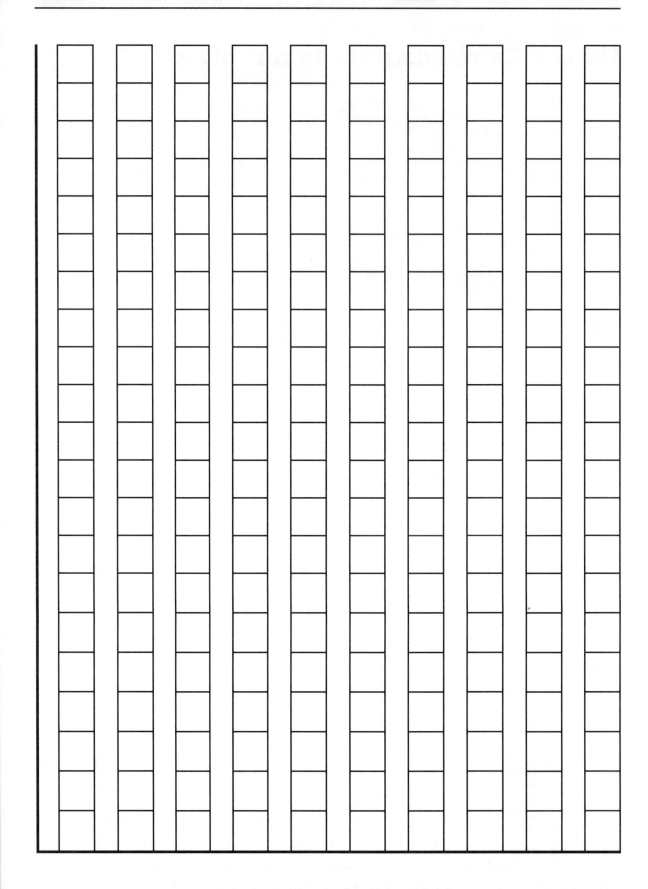

Name _____   Date _____

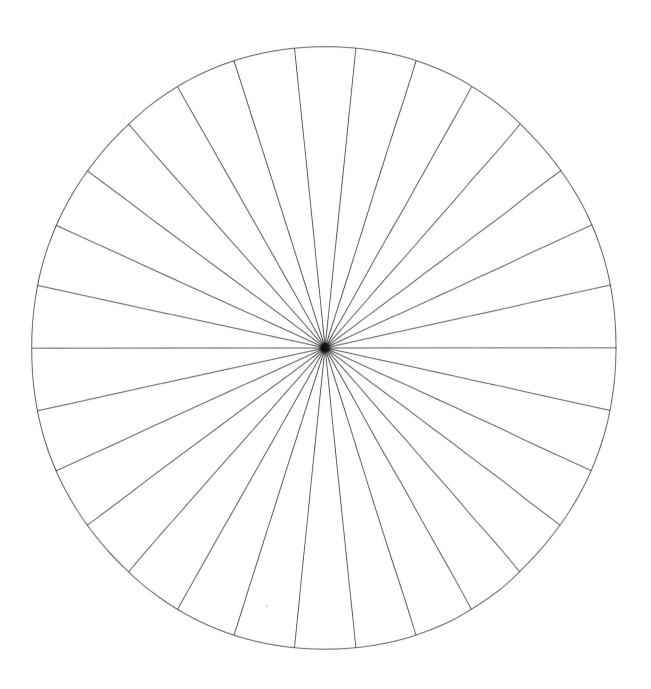

Name   Date

MATHS SKILLS FOR SCIENCE: YEARS 5&6

Name Date

	Tally	Total

Notes

RESOURCE SHEET

TALLY CHART

PHOTOCOPIABLE

Name _____   Date _____

Date _____

Today I have completed an activity called

_____

This activity is about _____

_____

From this work I have learned _____

_____

Date _____

Today I have completed an activity called

_____

This activity is about _____

_____

From this work I have learned _____

_____

Date _____

Today I have completed an activity called

_____

This activity is about _____

_____

From this work I have learned _____

_____